With best wishes to
Lawrence and Felicity

from Dennis
and Sylvia

LONDON
SCIENCE

*Museums, libraries, and places of
scientific, technological & medical interest*

LONDON COUNTY COUNCIL
THOMAS
YOUNG
1773 - 1829
MAN OF SCIENCE
lived here

LONDON COUNTY COUNCIL
CHARLES
3RD EARL
STANHOPE
1753 - 1816
REFORMER AND
INVENTOR
lived here

LONDON COUNTY COUNCIL
WILLIAM
BLIGH
1754 - 1817
COMMANDER
OF THE
"BOUNTY"
LIVED HERE

GREATER LONDON COUNCIL
SIR
RONALD
ROSS
1857 - 1932
Nobel Laureate
Discoverer of the
mosquito transmission
of malaria
lived here

LONDON COUNTY COUNCIL
QUINTIN
HOGG
1845 - 1903
Founder of the
Polytechnic Regent Street
lived here
1885 - 1898

A **PRION** GUIDE

LONDON SCIENCE

*Museums, libraries, and places of
scientific, technological & medical interest*

Dennis and Sylvia Rosen

Acknowledgements

We are particularly grateful to COPUS (Committee on the Public Understanding of Science) for providing a grant which enabled us to undertake the project of assembling the information for this guide. We thank the Curators and Librarians of the museums and other institutions we have visited for the help and assistance that all of them gave so willingly. Special thanks are due to Philip Maxwell for some initial discussions about the project; also to Alan Berman, Joan and Tony Booth, Alan Mackay, Vivian Moses, Keith Paton, Michael de Podesta, Bill Smith and to our sons and daughter, Nicholas, Richard and Rebecca, all of whom read parts of the text, tried out some of the walks and invariably made invaluable comments, corrections and suggestions which have been incorporated. Any remaining errors are ours.

Dennis and Sylvia Rosen
London, 1994

Published in the United Kingdom 1994 by PRION, an imprint of Multimedia Books Limited
32-34 Gordon House Road, London NW5 1LP

Managing Editor: Anne Johnson
Designer: Megra Mitchell
Picture Research: Julia Hanson
Production: Hugh Allan

A catalogue record for this book is available from The British Library.

ISBN 1-85375-140-5

10 9 8 7 6 5 4 3 2 1

Origination by Typongraph, Italy
Printed in Italy by Imago

Contents

FOREWORD

O f all its diverse qualities, London's position as a centre for science is perhaps the least known or understood. It is extraordinary that this should be so when you consider that in a sense the world begins and ends here, about the Prime Meridian at Greenwich. This line from pole to pole is the invisible monument to one of mankind's greatest and most fruitful scientific achievements. Its visible expression is the Old Royal Observatory and all it contains, including the great Harrison marine timekeepers and the transit telescope that defines the line itself.

In fact, science is everywhere in London: its practice, its people, its history, its ghosts. The Royal Society, the Royal Botanic Gardens at Kew, the colleges and institutes of the University of London, the Wellcome Foundation and dozens more nurture world-class science. Every major branch of scientific enquiry, of medicine, engineering and technology has its place in London, in the headquarters of institutions, in the conferences and meetings held here. Contemporary London is in every sense a world centre where, as has been the case for centuries, the shaping of tomorrow takes place today.

Its scientific credentials stem from a distinguished past, unparalleled in any other city in the world. 'London may be only ten hours away from Paris, but a trip to the British capital teaches you more than exploring the polar ice-caps or the interior of Africa,' wrote Elisée Reclus in 1860, encouraging the visitor from France to appreciate something of the intellectual attractions of London in the years after the Great Exhibition.

The Exhibition itself had been a remarkable success. It was the brainchild of Prince Albert, Queen Victoria's Consort, and reflected his belief in the importance of science to the wealth and future prosperity of the nation. As the world's first expo, it also established the model for those that were to follow. Science and innovation, made accessible to a wide audience, have been recurring themes.

But unlike some later shows the 1851 Exhibition made a profit, of £186,436. This was used to purchase land south of Kensington Gore, with the object of establishing there institutions devoted 'to the furtherance of industrial pursuits of all nations', including what were later described as 'Museums or Schools of Science and Industry'. Another outcome was the setting up by the Government of the Science and Art Department in 1853 with Lyon Playfair, distinguished chemist and scientific administrator, as Science Secretary. He was one of those who recognized that Britain would 'recede as an industrial nation, unless her population became more conversant with science than they are now.'

The outcome was the unique cultural estate, colloquially known as Albertopolis, which has become the home of some of London's most important scientific and artistic institutions. The Science Museum itself derives from the South Kensington Museum of 1857 which was to split into two at the end of the nineteenth century, the art collections forming the basis for the Victoria & Albert Museum, the sciences staying on the west side of Exhibition Road. Here are to be found collections that provide a vivid insight into the progress of humanity over the last two to three hundred years. These collections chart the rise of Britain as the first industrial nation in the middle years of the eighteenth century and its position as 'workshop of the world' in the nineteenth. Next door the

The Science Museum façade at night.

Natural History Museum holds a similar position of pre-eminence with its outstanding holdings in the natural and earth sciences while to the north stands Imperial College of Science, Technology and Medicine, Britain's, and Europe's, leading research and teaching institution in the field.

Albertopolis holds metaphors and messages for much of what we wish to be as a nation. It brings together the arts and the sciences in an increasingly fruitful union. It represents the highest standards in its research and teaching, and it is a place for the public that they may enjoy and gain inspiration from the excellence and achievements of the past and the present in order to have a better vision of the future.

In 1738, when Baron Pöllnitz described London as 'that city where true liberty bears rule; where the arts and sciences are cultivated and protected; where the inhabitants enjoy the goods of fortune without vain ostentation; where merit is considered and birth highly valued, when accompanied with virtue,' the benefits of the scientific revolution were already becoming apparent. The Royal Society was more than seventy-five years old, Newton – the site of whose home in Jermyn Street is, quite properly, marked with a blue plaque – had been dead for eleven years. London was already the city of science.

Today we stress the need for public understanding, such is our belief that as a unique discourse science, and the technologies that derive from it, require special cultivation in the minds of the population as a whole. Dennis and Sylvia Rosen, with the support of COPUS, the Committee for the Public Understanding of Science, provide in this book an invaluable insight into London as the home of science.

Neil Cossons
Director
The Science Museum, London

INTRODUCTION

London and Science

Research in London's scientific, medical, and engineering laboratories in this century has led, among other advances, to the discovery of penicillin, computerized tomography (CT scanning), holograms, and the structure of DNA. The immense importance of these discoveries was recognized by the award of Nobel prizes. In all, about twenty people have received a Nobel prize for work carried out in London laboratories. The work recognized by these awards has covered an immense range and has contributed to placing London in the forefront of international science.

When Wordsworth paused on Westminster Bridge on a September morning in 1802 and marvelled at the ships, towers, domes, theatres and temples of London lying before him, we may be reasonably sure that he paid no thought to the laboratories and engineers' offices that were to be found among the other buildings. He may not even have brought to mind the hospitals and physicians' consulting rooms. Yet had the Nobel prizes been instituted at the beginning of the nineteenth century instead of at the beginning of the twentieth, in London at that time there were scientists, engineers and physicians who would surely have been awarded them.

Wordsworth paused early in the morning, while the city lay still. Later in the day he might have found Humphrey Davy pursuing his researches in the laboratory at the Royal Institution and Henry Cavendish in the one he had set up in his house in Clapham.

Left: Westminster Bridge and the Houses of Parliament seen from the bank of the Thames behind St Thomas's Hospital. The present bridge replaced the one on which Wordsworth stood and was completed in 1862.

Right: The Royal Naval College, Greenwich, formerly known as the Royal Naval Hospital and built to a plan by Sir Christopher Wren.

Joseph Banks lived in Soho Square and was President of the Royal Society; his extensive collections of botanical, zoological and geological specimens were to form the core of the Natural History Museum. Marc Brunel, who had recently arrived in London, was working with Henry Maudslay on the design of machinery for the mass production of naval block and tackle before turning his attention to the project of a tunnel beneath the Thames, the world's first publicly accessible underwater tunnel. John Rennie was starting to sketch out the designs for new bridges across the Thames at Waterloo and Southwark. Edward Jenner was in London to seek volunteers who might benefit from his discovery of the procedure of vaccination.

At the beginning of the nineteenth century, London was a centre of study, but not yet a major teaching centre. Medical and surgical instruction was available. Also, colleges had been established largely for the military purposes of the realm — the Royal Laboratory and the Royal Military Academy at Woolwich to develop new explosives and to deal with the army's engineering needs, the Royal Naval College at Greenwich to teach the art and science of navigation, and the Royal Veterinary College at Camden Town which had been established to deal with farming problems but at that time was most occupied with methods of looking after the army's horses.

Widely-ranging instruction, which acknowledged the sciences, could be found only in the occasional lectures given at Gresham College in the City. Gresham College was founded in 1597 by the benefaction of Sir Thomas Gresham to encourage study, teaching and research in Divinity, Music, Astronomy, Geometry, Rhetoric, Law and Physic.

Later in the century, the spirit of the age forced the foundation of schools, colleges and institutes. These developed into the modern establishments that today make London a world centre of higher education. The University of London was founded in 1828 and followed by a succession of mechanics' institutes, polytechnics, medical and dental schools, and other places of advanced instruction.

With the passage of time, some of these have been lost, but most have flourished and indeed have developed to university level, often after having absorbed some of the smaller

places. On the day of Wordsworth's sonnet, there was no university in London; in the year 2000 there will be at least twelve universities, all with important science and engineering departments. Altogether, the universities of London teach each year about 180,000 students, of whom about a third study science, engineering, medicine and medically-related subjects, or computer sciences. In addition to the universities, there are many specialized centres of instruction, offering diplomas in various branches of science and engineering.

Before the nineteenth-century universities appeared, only the physicians and apothecaries, like the lawyers and divines, were normally the product of a formal education in their subject. The scientists and engineers were for the most part self-taught, except for the mathematicians. The specialists, however, tended to come together to form associations. These were initially for the exchange of information; some later were for the protection and regulation of particular specialities. The first and most important of them was the Royal Society, founded in 1662 by King Charles II at the instigation of a group of men interested in the then new ideas of acquiring knowledge by experimentation. The prestige as well as the political power of the Royal Society, and the interest of its Fellows in all branches of learning, inhibited the formation of other scientific societies for almost a century and a half.

In 1802, the Linnean Society was the only other established scientific society. It had been founded in 1788 for the study of botany and zoology only because of the purchase by its first president of the collection of specimens left in Sweden by Linnaeus on his death. In the first decades of the nineteenth century, however, entomologists, geologists, astronomers and others had set up their own societies, often with royal patronage. By the end of the century, every major scientific, medical and engineering discipline had a society or association based in London, arranging meetings and publishing proceedings or transactions. By the end of the twentieth century, these developments have spread to encompass even the most minor disciplines, each of which has its own society, association or meeting group, although in some cases the high costs of London offices have driven them into the provinces.

The industrial revolution, universal education, and the complexity of urban living created the demand for centres of scientific information, alongside the teaching centres and learned societies. Starting in the late eighteenth century — and at an accelerating pace in the nineteenth and twentieth — museums, libraries, botanic gardens, herbariums, zoos and now electronic data banks were established, sometimes privately, but most often by national or local government.

At the same time, scientific experimentation moved from the rich amateur's domestic laboratory to the university laboratories and then expanded from there to laboratories and

research centres with special interests, funded either by governmental agencies or by industry. The vigorous London culture of scientific, engineering and medical development gave rise in turn to a thriving trade in instruments, chemical reagents, laboratory accessories, and medical and surgical requisites. There was, too, engineering manufacture on all scales, from the lightest to the very heavy and also the publication and sale of scientific and technical books.

However, the growth of scientific London took time. In that time, generations of scientists, engineers, physicians and surgeons came on to the stage, made their contribution, and after death left sometimes a named law, effect, disease, procedure, or construction, and sometimes only a memory.

Yet traces often remain, even without a professionally immortalized name. In some cases, a

Opposite: Statue of Florence Nightingale by A. G. Walker. part of the Crimea Memorial in Waterloo Place.

Above: The house of the Royal Society in Carlton House Terrace.

Right: The Sir Joseph Banks Building at the Royal Botanic Gardens. Kew.

plaque marks the house where a contributor lived; in others, a gravestone marks the place where his or her remains lie after death. The most eminent may have a statue or bust or portrait displayed in a public place; and in a few cases a memory is preserved in the name of a building or a street.

The legacy of the scientific past of London and the resonances of its dynamic present provide a very rich mixture. Here and throughout this guide, science is meant to include medicine and engineering as well as the academic natural sciences. To give an account within the space available, we have been obliged to confine ourselves strictly to the area covered by the inner and outer London boroughs (the administrative area of the former Greater London Council). This guidebook presents a selection of what can be seen and experienced within that territory for those setting out on the adventure of exploring London's science.

CHAPTER 1
REPOSITORIES OF SCIENCE
Museums of the Natural Sciences, Medicine and Engineering

Landon has been a major world centre of scientific study for many centuries. In former times, the discarded apparatus and unpublished records of science were often neglected and then lost. But the more rapidly the sciences advance and change the world, the more two matters are realized.

The first is how much people need explanations of what the sciences are about — what they say of the world around us. The second is how much a study of past sciences helps to understand their present position. As a result, the number of museums presenting this information has grown steadily over the past century.

In the early 1630s, John Tradescant, the gardener and botanical collector, established in Lambeth what he called his Ark. It was the first museum of scientific and miscellaneous curiosities opened to the public in London. Today, to our surprise, we have found more than sixty museums, apart from the great scientific collections in the Science Museum and the Natural History Museum, either with specialist collections or with general collections that include objects to be recommended for their scientific interest.

Tradescant's museum was later lost to London. His collections were acquired by Elias Ashmole and became the foundation of the Ashmolean Museum in Oxford. The private collections of others, however, have remained in the capital. The great collection of Hans Sloane formed the foundation of the British Museum in the eighteenth century. In the nineteenth century, the British Museum acquired, among many others, the collection of Joseph Banks. Large parts of the Sloane and Banks collections ended up in the Natural

History Museum. Similarly, thousands of specimens that John Hunter brought together as a teaching resource in his anatomy school at the end of the eighteenth century formed the core of the Hunterian Museum of the Royal College of Surgeons. Those of Hunter's specimens that survived damage during the 1939-1945 war are still used for teaching purposes today at the Royal College of Surgeons.

Significant private collecting has continued through the years. It has led to the foundation of, among others, the several Wellcome Museums and the Horniman Museum, named after Henry Wellcome and Frederick Horniman. And Gerald Wells, the curator of the Vintage Wireless Museum, continues to add to the unusual and astonishing collection he has assembled in his own house.

Furthermore, many museums continue to benefit from donations on a smaller scale made by private collectors. This is the case for the well-known public museums and it is especially true for many private museums which have been established by colleges and societies.

Because the richness and variety of the private museums add so much to the culture of London, most of those of scientific or medical interest have been included in this chapter. Indeed, they account for a third of the total. It is to be stressed, however, that the private nature of these museums must be respected. The details given in the following pages state explicitly whether admission is restricted. Where it is, the restriction is usually to people who have a professional connection with the subject of the museum, or who are engaged in research which can be assisted by use of the museum's collections.

In all these cases, it is necessary for intending visitors to apply well beforehand, preferably by letter, to the curator of the museum in question, requesting permission to study the collection. This permission will readily be granted to all who have a suitable reason for the request.

Most museums, whether public or private, have a salespoint where picture postcards, booklets, etc., can be bought. Most allow photography, but many do not have restaurants or an associated library. The museum details mention exceptions only where relevant.

Where there is an admission charge, £ means a charge of less than £1, ££ means between £1 and £3.50, and £££ means more than £3.50. If concessions are indicated, children, students, and people who are unemployed or who are of pensionable age may be admitted at reduced rates.

Above: Main entrance to the British Museum, Great Russell Street.

Opposite: The Tradescant tomb, Museum of Garden History, St Mary's Church, Lambeth.

Alexander Fleming Laboratory Museum

St Mary's Hospital, Praed Street, W2 1NY
Tel: 071-725 6528

Underground: Paddington, Edgware Road
Rail: Paddington
Bus: 7, 15, 27, 36

Opening times: Mon-Thur 10.00-13.00 (other times by appointment)
Admission: ££

Photography: not allowed
Group visits: write to or telephone the Curator
Hospital and Medical School archives can be seen on request

The working area of the laboratory in which Fleming discovered penicillin has been recreated as it was in the summer of 1928 when the event took place. At the time, Fleming was professor of bacteriology in the medical school and the tiny room was his office as well as his scientific workplace. Long before his award of the Nobel Prize for Medicine, Fleming had begun to make his name as a research scientist, but was given only the most meagre facilities.

Eventually, Fleming was allotted more spacious accommodation and the laboratory was used for hospital purposes. In climbing the narrow stairs now to the restored laboratory, a wrong turn would lead into one of the hospital wards. But the museum, when reached, displays the bacteriologist's bench, with microscope and other tools of the trade.

The workbench in the reconstruction of Alexander Fleming's laboratory.

Also, of course, there is the window in front of which Fleming left the petri dish with the staphylococcus growth on which a spore of *Penicillium notatum* landed and, in growing and killing off the bacteria, started Fleming's hunt. Probably, however, the spore's route in was not through the window, but up the staircase from the laboratory of some mycologists working on the floor below.

In rooms above the laboratory, displays present the background of Fleming's work. A short video film shows scenes from his life.

Bethlem Royal Hospital Archives and Museum

The Bethlem Royal Hospital, Monks Orchard Road,
Beckenham, Kent BR3 3BX
Tel: 081-776 4307

Rail: Eden Park, East Croydon
Bus: 119, 166, 194
Free car parking

Opening times: Mon-Fri 9.30-17.30
(intending visitors should always telephone first to ensure that the museum will be open)
Admission: free, but contributions welcome

Archives: open for research by prior appointment
Access for wheelchairs
Group visits: write to or telephone the Archivist and Curator
Photography: allowed only by arrangement with the Archivist and Curator

The Bethlem Royal Hospital, whence the word Bedlam entered the language, was founded as a priory in the middle of the thirteenth century and has been devoted to care of the insane since the late fourteenth century. It was originally located just outside the walls of the City of London, first in Bishopsgate then in Moorfields. It moved in 1815 to the building now occupied by the Imperial War Museum (see p.41) and to its present site in 1930.

In 750 years it has accumulated a variety of treasures, objects of interest and archival material of historical importance. The museum is tiny and has space for only a fraction of the material that the hospital possesses, but from Moorfields there is a display of devices used to restrain the insane, sculptures by Cibber of *Raving Madness* and *Melancholy Madness* which surmounted the gates,

Broach Schizophrene, *oil on canvas, by Bryan Charnley (1949-1991), an artist who suffered from schizophrenia.*

and evocative alms boxes for collecting funds to sustain the hospital. On display, also, is an important collection of paintings and drawings, mainly by artists who suffered mental disorders, including works by Richard Dadd, Jonathan Martin, Nijinsky, Charles Sims and Louis Wain.

Grief or Sorrow, *watercolour on paper, by Richard Dadd (1817-1886), an inmate of the Bethlem Royal Hospital.*

BOC Museum: Charles King Collection of Anaesthetics

9 Bedford Square, WC1B 3RA
Tel: 071-631 1650

Underground: Goodge Street, Tottenham Court Road
Rail: Euston, St Pancras, King's Cross
Bus: 10, 14, 14A, 24, 29, 73, 134

Opening times: Wed-Fri 9.00-17.00
Admission: only to professionally interested visitors, arranged by prior appointment with
the Curator or Librarian

Library: admission only by prior appointment and at the discretion of the Librarian
Access-for wheelchairs
Group visits: write to or telephone the Librarian
Photography: not allowed

Charles King (1888-1966) was the leading British manufacturer and supplier of anaesthetic equipment in the middle part of the present century. He was so interested in his vocation that he was led to amass a very considerable collection of anaesthetic and other medical materials which, after various temporary homes, has now been deposited with the Association of Anaesthetists.

Only a small part of the collection can be displayed at any one time in the small basement museum in the Association's premises, but the display is rotated on an annual basis. Items range from eighteenth-century resuscitation devices, through primitive drop methods of anaesthetic delivery, to the most modern systems of anaesthetic application. There are also several objects relating to blood transfusion and saline infusion.

The displays are presented with great clarity and can be both instructive and illuminating to those with a basic knowledge of anaesthetic technology.

Apparatus, designed by Dr Thomas Small, for inducing anaesthesia during childbirth, using either ether or trichlorethylene.

British Dental Association Museum

64 Wimpole Street, W1M 8AL
Tel: 071-935 0875

Underground: Oxford Circus, Regent's Park, Bond Street
Bus: 6, 7, 10, 13, 113

Opening times: Mon-Fri 10.00-17.00
Admission: only to professionally interested visitors, arranged by prior appointment with the Curator

Library: admission only by prior appointment and at the discretion of the Librarian
Group visits: write to or telephone the Museum Officer
Photography: not allowed

A dental surgery of 1860, reconstructed in this evocative museum, is like a Victorian drawing room with the addition of a spittoon for collecting blood and a round table with drawers containing the dentist's probes, burrs, extractors and other instruments. Even one of forty years later seems more domestic than clinical, although it has, discreetly tucked away in a corner, a foot-treadle power source for drilling and a chair with anaesthetic gases in cylinders beneath. But the display of dental engines, more elaborate anaesthetic apparatus, and dental X-ray machines, obliges one to remember the high technology of dental practice.

The old instruments are artistically displayed in carefully graded arrays of size and shape, and artificial teeth are similarly arranged by size, shape, colour and material. However, the artistry of the display is not sufficient to make you forget that the modern machines, engines and tools make a visit to the dentist today incomparably less painful than a few decades ago.

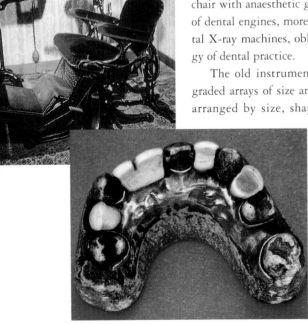

Above left: Reconstruction of a dentist's surgery. circa 1860.

Left: Upper denture with gold base and ivory teeth, made for the Duke of Clarence by Isaac Wilson of Bath, circa 1810.

A thirteenth-century European astrolabe.

British Museum

Great Russell Street, WC1 3DG
Tel: 071-636 1555

Underground: Tottenham Court Road, Russell Square, Holborn
Rail: Euston, St Pancras, King's Cross
Bus: 10, 14, 14A, 24, 29, 73, 134 (Tottenham Court Road northbound
and Gower Street southbound) 68, 188 (Southampton Row)
7, 8, 19, 25, 38, 55 (New Oxford Street)

Opening times: Mon-Sat 10.00-17.00, Sun 14.30-18.00
Admission: free, but donations welcome

Restaurant
Library: admission only with Reader's Ticket
Access for wheelchairs
Group visits: write to or telephone the Education Services Department (071-323 8511)
Photography: allowed, but only without flash

Despite having split off the Natural History Museum and, at least temporarily, the Museum of Mankind, the British Museum has a large display of science, medicine and engineering. The museum is well known to hold large collections of tools and weaponry from most of the recorded civilizations of ancient and medieval history (and somewhat more recent far-eastern kingdoms). But it also holds a surprising amount of scientific objects in its collections of clocks and old instruments (Galleries 43 and 44).

With 500 clocks and chronometers and 4,000 watches, this is one of the best collections in the world, giving an unbroken account of the development of domestic horology. There are about 500 items in the collection of old mathematical and astronomical instruments, including European astrolabes (Room 42) dating back to *circa* 1200. There are even older instruments in the museum's Arabic collection.

One item of high importance to present science is the 2,000-year-old corpse of Lindow Man (Room 39), particularly well-preserved by immersion in a bog in Cheshire and able to reveal much about his genetics and living pattern. Also to be noted are some of the earliest-known medical prescriptions, on Egyptian papyri of about 1200 BC (Room 62). In Room 69, devoted to life in ancient Rome and Greece, there are Roman medical implements of the first century AD. Cryptographers may also like to see the Rosetta Stone (Room 25), which allowed Champollion and Young to elucidate Egyptian hieroglyphics.

Above: the Rosetta Stone, bearing an inscription in hieroglyphic, demotic and Greek, allowed Champollion and Young to understand the writing and language of ancient Egypt.

Right: Gold portable sundial by Thomas Tompion (1639-1713).

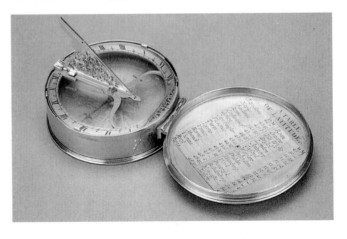

British Optical Museum

c/o The British College of Optometrists,
10 Knaresborough Place, SW5 0TG
Tel: 071-373 7765

Underground: Earl's Court, Gloucester Road
Bus: 31, 74

Opening times: Mon-Fri 10.00-16.00
Admission: free, but only by prior appointment with the Librarian

Library
Arrangements for group/school visits: contact the Librarian

The British College of Optometrists was created in 1980. It succeeded the British Optical Association from which it acquired the present museum collection and the nucleus of a useful professional library, as well as major professional administrative duties. The museum was created by J. H. Sutcliffe, a passionate collector of spectacles and other optical devices long before the collectability of such items was generally appreciated.

As a result, there is assembled in the museum a large collection of spectacles and spectacle cases, lorgnettes, quizzing glasses and spy glasses, as well as old ophthalmoscopes and other instruments for eye examinations. The spectacles date back to the sixteenth century and include leather-framed specimens of the seventeenth century. The spectacles of the eighteenth and nineteenth centuries show surprising technical accomplishment.

Many of the spectacles and the cases made to hold them, and also the opera glasses, lorgnettes, and other aids, are beautifully decorated. This makes them art treasures as well as objects of interest to the history of science and optometry.

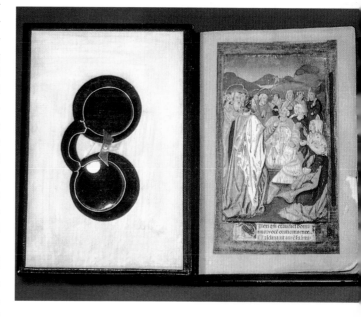

Fifteenth-century Book of Hours *with gold-framed spectacles inset into the front cover (replica).*

Diagrammatic illustration of Brunel's Tunnel in cross-section, showing Brunel's method of boring a tunnel and the tunnel's position in relation to the bed of the Thames.

Brunel's Engine House

Railway Avenue, Tunnel Road, SE16 4LF
Tel: 081-318 2489

Underground: Rotherhithe (East London Line)
Rail: New Cross (then East London Line)
Bus: 47, 188, P11

Opening times: first Sunday of each month, 12.00-16.00, or by appointment
Admission: ££ (concessions)

Group visits: write to or telephone the Director (0708 447361)

This building was erected to house the engines that originally extracted the spoil during the digging of the Wapping-Rotherhithe foot tunnel. Marc Brunel conceived and designed the project; his son, Isambard Kingdom Brunel, was the chief engineer; and it was built between 1825 and 1843.

The tunnel was the first anywhere to allow people to pass under water and was hailed at the time as the eighth wonder of the world. After the excavations were completed, the building housed pumps to extract the seepage water. This use continued when the tunnel

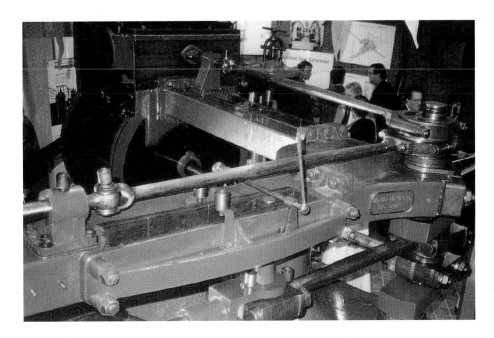

was incorporated into the London underground railway system, originally running steam trains. However, when the line was electrified in 1913, electric pumps situated elsewhere replaced the old steam pumps for the extraction of water.

The building now houses a small exhibition explaining the origin of the tunnel and describing its various technical details. A 15-minute video presentation shows many of the most interesting images and details of the tunnel and its history, not otherwise available to the visitor.

Above: Interior view of Brunel's Engine House, with the only surviving example of a compound V pumping engine, built in 1882 by J. & G. Rennie.

Left: Exterior view of Brunel's Engine House, with a modern replica of the original chimney, but the original brickwork of the main shaft (bottom right).

BT Museum — The Story of Telecommunications

145 Queen Victoria Street, EC4V 4AT
Tel: 071-248 7444

Underground: Blackfriars
Rail: Blackfriars
Bus: 45, 59, 63, 149, 172, 609 (to Blackfriars);
4, 11, 15, 15B, X15, 17, 23, 26, 76, 521 (to St Paul's)
Car park (paying, nearby)

Opening times: Mon-Fri 10.00-17.00
Admission: free

Library: admission only by prior appointment
Access for wheelchairs
Photography: allowed, but not for publication
Group visits: telephone Museum office

A visitor to the Museum, operating an old sleeve-control switchboard, recovered from the Romford Exchange.

This specialized but excellent museum presents an account of powered communication over distances. The account looks back as far as the late eighteenth century and forward to the early twenty-first. There are an ancient semaphore telegraph, numerous examples of electric telegraphy, telephones by the score, and videophones. Diagrams and models are shown of networks connected by old-fashioned wire cables, optical fibres and radio links. There are fax machines ancient and modern, though only limited mention of broadcasting by radio or television.

By use of working models, experiments operated by the push of a button, or by well-presented videos, some of which are interactive, clear explanations are given of the ways in which the various devices work. Furthermore, displays show how communications are likely to develop in the near future.

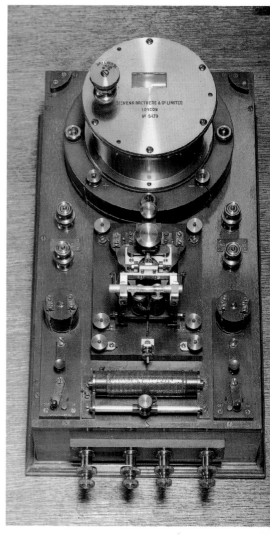

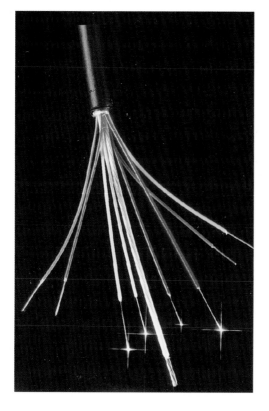

Above: This early radio receiver is a Maskelyne-type coherer of 1905, capable of detecting pulses as in Morse code, but not speech.

Left: An optical fibre cable with the end splayed to show its structure.

Chelsea Physic Garden

66 Royal Hospital Road, SW3 4BS
Tel: 071-352 5646

Underground: Sloane Square
Rail: Victoria
Bus: 239 (to door), 11, 19, 22 (to King's Road)

Opening times: April-October, Wednesdays and Sundays 14.00-18.00
Admission: ££

Restaurant
Library: admission only by prior appointment
Access for wheelchairs
Group visits: write to or telephone the Education Officer

Other botanical gardens founded in the sixteenth and seventeenth centuries were annexes of medical schools. This one, however, was independently established in 1673 by the Worshipful Society of Apothecaries.

The Society was a guild of the City of London and somewhat at odds, at that time, with the College of Physicians which was seeking to control medical education. The place was called a Physic Garden to emphasize that its purpose was to assist the teaching of the

The garden area named after Philip Miller, gardener to the Society of Apothecaries 1722-1770, and containing some of the plants introduced into cultivation by him, including salvia and geum.

art of curative medicine (physic) by means of herbal remedies. Apothecaries, from the seventeenth to the nineteenth centuries, filled a role of general practitioners as well as dispensers of drugs and the Society took considerable care to maintain professional standards.

An early student in the garden was Hans Sloane who learned botany there in about 1679 before going to Paris and Montpellier to study medicine. By 1722, when Sloane was established as a rich and successful physician and President of the Royal Society, he was able to refound the Garden under terms that assured the health of its finances. A fine marble statue of Sloane by Rysbrack was set up in the centre of the Garden in 1748; the original was moved to the entrance hall of the British Museum in 1985 and was replaced at Chelsea by a replica.

Sloane appointed as chief gardener Philip Miller who, in a career of nearly fifty years, became the leading botanical horticulturist of his time. An area in the westernmost corner of the Garden commemorates Miller and some of the plants introduced into this country by him, many of which are now commonly cultivated. Other important botanists associated with the Garden are remembered in adjacent areas, often by plants that officially bear their names: *Forsythia*, *Banksia*, *Fortunearia*, and others.

About a third of the area of the Garden is taken up with order beds in which more than sixty plant families are laid out systematically as a major aid to botanical learning. Many beds, in addition, are devoted to plants specifically of medical application, currently and formerly in orthodox western medicine, in western homeopathic practice, and in various traditions — Chinese, Indian, Maori, and others. A bed of poisonous plants serves to teach visitors what to avoid and detective story writers how to twist their plots.

Among other items of pride in the Garden is the largest outdoor olive tree in Britain, one of the oldest rock-gardens in Europe, constructed in 1773, a storax tree (*Styrax officinalis*) which may have been one of the original specimens when the Garden was first established, and an important collection of many ferns which are housed in the Thomas Moore Cool Fernery.

Statue of Sir Hans Sloane by Rysbrack.

Clock and Watch Collection of the Worshipful Company of Clockmakers

Guildhall Library, Aldermansbury, EC2P 2EJ
Tel: 071-332 1868/1870

Underground: Bank, St Paul's, Moorgate, Mansion House
Rail: Liverpool Street, Moorgate
Bus: 4, 8, 11, 15B, 21, 22B, 25, 26, 43, 76, 133, 172, 214, 501

Opening times: Mon-Fri 9.30-16.45
Admission: free

Library
Access for wheelchairs
Photography: only by permission from the Curator

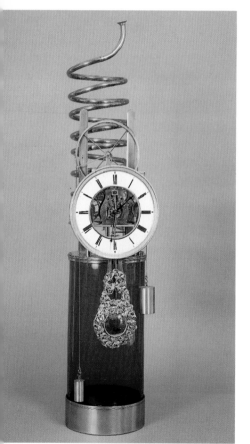

This small exhibition, housed in a room of the Guildhall adjacent to the Guildhall Library and Bookshop, presents an astonishingly rich collection of timepieces. The earliest date from the fifteenth century. But there are examples from all the centuries since then and, in particular, from most of the great British clock makers — Ramsey, Tompion, Harrison, Graham and others — many of whom served as Master of the Clockmakers' Company.

Among the exhibits are examples using every variety of escapement. Of special scientific interest are: a seventeenth-century astronomical table clock by Samuel Watson, reputed to have belonged to Newton; one of Harrison's original marine chronometers, tested by George III in person before Harrison was allowed to collect the prize of £20,000 which had been offered by the Admiralty for a clock accurate enough to allow a reliable determination of longitude at sea; and a remarkable Italian clock of 1835, powered by the hydrogen evolved when zinc pellets are dropped periodically into a glass jar of sulphuric acid.

The chemical clock, powered by the hydrogen gas evolved when zinc pellets are released from the coiled tube and fall into the glass jar of sulphuric acid.

Crossness Sewage Treatment Works and Pumping Station

Crossness, Abbey Wood, SE2 9AQ
Tel: 081-507 4802

Rail: Abbey Wood
Bus: 178, 272
Free car parking

Opening times: Mon-Fri 9.30-16.00
Admission: free but strictly only by prior appointment

Access for wheelchairs

I n the early 1860s, the Thames was an open sewer running through London. Because all the drains and effluents were emptied directly into it, it was not only without fish, but also the stench was so foul that the curtains of the House of Commons were soaked in chloride of lime ($CaOCl_2$) when the members were sitting, to mitigate the 'Great Stink'. There were plans to move the parliament to Hampton Court and the courts of law to Oxford or St Albans. The situation was saved when the Metropolitan Board of Works (the forerunner of the London County Council, which became the Greater London Council until its abolition in 1986) commissioned the construction of great new sewers, north and south of the river, to carry the sewage to outflows far downstream.

Sir Joseph Bazalgette was the remarkable engineer of this work and Crossness was his site on the south bank of the river for rudimentary treatment of the sewage before its discharge into the river. His corresponding site on the north bank was at Beckton, close to where, a few years later, the Gas Light and Coke Company established its major site for the production of town gas.

The Prince of Wales opened the Crossness Pumping Station in 1865. At that time the engines merely lifted the effluent to a temporary storage tank from which, at high tide, it could be conveniently discharged into the river. In the succeeding century and a quarter, not only have Bazalgette's pumping engines been superseded by more modern pumps, but the treatment of sewage has been developed as a large-scale technological process. Responsibility for dealing with sewage has passed to Thames Water plc which, both before and since privatization, has been controlling a plan of massive capital investment. This has involved

An aerial view of the Crossness site.

the erection of the elaborate facilities that now occupy a sizeable part of the 450 acre (180 ha) Crossness site.

THE SEWAGE TREATMENT WORKS

About 680 megalitres of sewage each day (where each litre weighs about a kilogram) flows into Crossness. The material is first screened to remove large objects of wood, metal or plastic. It then passes to settlement tanks — a dozen and a half of them, each as big as a large swimming pool — where, in a few hours, sedimentation allows a separation of the relatively clear layer of liquid, the 'settled sewage', from the sediment, or 'sludge'. The sludge is consolidated and partially decomposed by bacteria to yield methane, which is burned to produce nearly sufficient electricity to run the whole site. The residue of the sludge is currently dumped at sea. However, EU regulations will forbid this practice from 1998 and, after the construction of incinerators at a cost of £90 million, it will then be burned. Meanwhile, the settled sewage is aerated, purified by bacterial action, and the safely-treated water is returned to the Thames.

These processes take place in scores of vast beds, pressure vessels, and settlement tanks, involving as well a power station and ships to carry the residual sludge out to sea. The whole operation of dealing with the waste of several million people, together with industrial sewage contributing five to ten per cent of the total, requires and displays chemical engineering technology on a monster scale.

THE OLD PUMPING STATION AND BEAM ENGINES

(This is in the care of the Crossness Engines Trust. For appointments to visit, contact the Secretary of the Trust, Mr Michael Dunmow, 8 Yorkland Avenue, Welling, Kent DA16 2LF (081-303 0723) or telephone Mr P. Skilton (0322 332195).)

Bazalgette's original Pumping Station is one of the few Grade I listed industrial buildings in the Greater London area. It houses four engines built by James Watt & Sons. Each

engine has a beam about 13 m in length and about 47 tons in weight; each would drive a flywheel over 8 m in diameter and would be capable of lifting 125 tons of sewage a minute. These magnificent relics of Victorian engineering have not been used since 1953, but are now being restored by volunteers.

The building in which they sit is magnificent on a scale to match the royal dignity of the engines which are named, respectively, Victoria, Prince Consort, Alexandra and Albert Edward. From the outside, the engine house seems to be a Florentine palace seen though Victorian eyes; inside, it is pure exuberant industrial Victorian. The spaces are sectioned off by elaborate ironwork grilles, the walkways are supported by iron pillars with floral ironwork decoration, and between the pillars hang pierced ironwork screens in which the initials of the Metropolitan Board of Works are interwoven with patterns of Moorish intricacy.

A section of the ironwork, recently repainted, in the Old Pumping Station.

Darwin Museum

Down House, Luxted Road, Downe, Kent BR6 7JT
Tel: 0689 859119

Rail: Bromley South, then by bus
Bus: 146 to Downe village, then walk approximately half a kilometre
Car park (free)

Opening times: Wed-Sun and Bank Holidays 13.00-17.00
Admission: ££ (concessions)

Access for wheelchairs
Group visits: only by prior arrangement with the Curator
Photography: allowed only in the garden

Of the various shrines to scientists, medical people and technologists in and around London, this is probably the most attractive. The house is the one in which Charles Darwin lived with his wife and children from 1842 until his death in 1882. Furthermore, it is the place where he wrote *On the Origin of the Species*, *Descent of Man* and several other major works. And it is the house he was increasingly reluctant to leave as he grew older. He travelled occasionally to the centre of London, or even further afield, but he often cited his health as a reason and excuse for staying in Downe. Its rural situation belies the fact that it stands within the official bounds of Greater London and so merits a place in this Guide.

The house is not exactly as it was when Darwin died — some small alterations have been made in the intervening century — but the disposition of the ground floor rooms (those now open to the public) remain as they were in his time and contain much of the original furniture. They certainly give, better than in most similar museums, a sense of how the house felt when Darwin lived there.

One room, the New Study, in the part of the house added a few years before Darwin's death, offers a well-presented display of ideas about the source of variety of the living world, from the Greeks to

Down House, where Darwin lived and spent nearly all his time for the last forty years of his life.

Darwin's contemporaries. There are also, in diagrammatic form round the walls, sketches of modern ideas of the time scale of the evolution of life on Earth. The other rooms are more domestic and personal. The Old Study is the centre of the shrine: the location of the writing of the *Origin*, with desk, chair, microscope, specimen cabinets, etc. more or less as they were then.

The Charles Darwin Room was in fact the dining room for most of Darwin's occupation of the house and now displays memorabilia of all kinds: hats, notebooks, a telescope, letters he wrote and received, etc. The Erasmus Darwin Room, the dining room when Darwin first moved into the house, but later the billiards room, is devoted to memorabilia of Darwin's grandfather, the eminent physician, scientist and inventor, and also a display of paintings of various members of the distinguished Darwin family. In the Drawing Room there is only one cabinet of mementoes, but an air of the modest wealth and comfort in which Darwin lived and worked.

The Drawing Room looks out, through the verandah, to a glorious and very spacious garden. A particular pleasure of a visit to the Darwin Museum is being able to take the walk out through the back of the garden, along a footpath bordering on open fields — the walk that Darwin paced back and forth daily for forty years, from twelve o'clock until one o'clock, in order, he said, to do his thinking.

At the village end of Luxted Road is the attractive thirteenth-century church of St Mary's and on the southern wall of its tower is a sundial placed in commemoration of Darwin. Within the church is a memorial to Sir John Lubbock (1803-1865), an amateur astronomer, first Vice-Chancellor of the University of London, Treasurer (1830-1835 and 1838-1845) and also Vice-President of the Royal Society. His son, who succeeded to the baronetcy and later was created the first Lord Avebury, was a distinguished biologist and anthropologist and a friend and supporter of Darwin. He was so distressed by the reaction of the then vicar of St Mary's to Darwin's theories that he transferred his place of worship to a church in a neighbouring parish.

The Old Study at Down House, where Darwin wrote On the Origin of the Species, *with his desk, chair, and other possessions.*

Opposite the church is a typical village pub, The Queen's Head, where the celebrated local resident is also remembered by the Darwin Bar: stop here for a drink if time allows.

Design Museum

Butlers Wharf, Shad Thames, SE1 2YD
Tel: 071-403 6933

Underground: Tower Hill, London Bridge
Rail: London Bridge, Tower Gateway
Bus: 15, 42, 47, 78, P11
Car park (paying)

Opening times: daily 10.30-17.30
Admission: ££ (concessions)

Restaurant
Library: admission only by prior appointment
Access for wheelchairs
Group visits: write to or telephone the Director
Photography: allowed, but without tripods

This modern museum, excitingly located beside the Thames and just down-river from Tower Bridge, has frequently-changing exhibitions and displays. These deal with most items of common use, such as cameras, cars, chairs, forks, knives, pans, plates, pots, radios, tables, television sets, toothbrushes, and so on. There are also well-known objects but not of common domestic use, such as motor bicycles and industrial lighting sources. Many items on show cannot fail to be of great interest to production engineers anxious about the aesthetic appeal of their factory output. Most of the items will arouse a reaction in every citizen: envy in some, scorn in others.

Also in the museum are interactive video and database systems, illustrating principles and practice of good design.

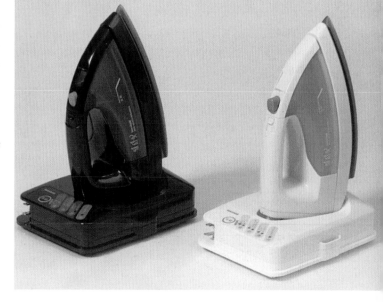

Cordless Steam Irons, manufactured by Matsushita Electric in the 1980s and displayed at the Museum.

Faraday Museum

The Royal Institution, 21 Albemarle Street, W1X 4BS
Tel: 071-409 2992

Underground: Green Park
Bus: 9, 14, 19, 22, 38

Opening times: Mon-Fri 13.00-16.00
Admission: £

Library: admission only by prior appointment
Group visits: write to or telephone the Librarian
Photography: not allowed

Michael Faraday (1791-1867) was one of the most prolific scientific discoverers in history and a major influence on the development of physics and chemistry in the nineteenth century. He spent all his scientific working life at the Royal Institution. The laboratory in which, in this building, he pursued his magnetic researches has been reconstructed as it was in his time.

Also on view are many important pieces of the apparatus he used, as well as many of his manuscripts, personal effects and various medals and decorations which were bestowed on him. On the walls of the corridor leading to the laboratory and museum, copies of drawings and documentary records give a vivid picture of Faraday's impoverished childhood background. They reveal the remarkable way in which he raised himself from a state of minimal education to become one of the world's leading experimental scientists.

The façade of the Royal Institution, from an early nineteenth-century aquatint by Hosmer Shepherd.

Coloured lithograph of Florence Nightingale in the Military Hospital at Scutari, in the Crimea.
This design was copied on to the £10 banknote in 1975.

Florence Nightingale Museum

St Thomas's Hospital, 2 Lambeth Palace Road, SE1 7EW
Tel: 071-620 0374

Underground: Waterloo, Westminster, Lambeth North
Rail: Waterloo
Bus: 12, 53, 77, 109, 171, 171A, 184, 196, 507, C1

Opening times: Tues-Sun and Bank Holidays
(except 25 Dec - 1 Jan, Good Friday and Easter Monday) 10.00-16.00
Admission: ££ (concessions)

Restaurant (in St Thomas's Hospital)
Access for wheelchairs
Group visits: write to or telephone the Director
Photography: not allowed

This museum is a personal tribute to Florence Nightingale, but it also offers an insight into several aspects of British history over the period of her long life (1820-1910). The displays include many details of her work for the British Army during the Crimean War (1854-1856), a general survey of her further work, after her return to England, for the improvement of various aspects of medical administration, and a selection of personal mementoes. A video film gives a balanced account of Florence Nightingale's life, but some of the images shown (exteriors and interiors of various houses with Nightingale connections) are without explanation.

Even though much of the material on display is personal to Florence Nightingale, informative glimpses are given of mid-nineteenth-century developments of aspects of medical care. Florence Nightingale played an important part in the development of hospital design, the training of nurses and midwives, the beginnings of community care and the inauguration of district nurse services.

A Turkish candle lantern, said to have been carried by Florence Nightingale through the hospital at Scutari.

Freud Museum

20 Maresfield Gardens, NW3 5SX
Tel: 071-435 2002/5167

Underground: Finchley Road
Rail: Finchley Road and Frognal
Bus: 13, 46, 82, 113, 268, C11, C12
Street car parking

Opening times: Wed-Sun 12.00-16.00
Admission: ££

Group visits: write to or telephone the Director
Photography: allowed without flash

The museum is the house in which Freud (1856-1939) spent the last year of his life. Its display provides a general hagiography of Freud, his wife, sister-in-law and daughter, with brief mention of his sons and various disciples. Display cabinets contain a large part of Freud's collection of antiquities, mostly unlabelled, and there is a bust of Freud and portraits by Salvador Dali and others.

20 Maresfield Gardens, NW3. Freud's last home and now the Freud Museum.

Freud's consulting room at Maresfield Gardens, with the patient's couch and the analyst's chair behind it.

In one room, a continuously playing video shows, firstly, pictures of Vienna in 1938, just before Freud and his family left, with the camera lingering over a set of still photographs showing interior views of the Freuds' apartment in Berggasse; and secondly, some home movies with occasional pictures of members of the Freud family and friends, but mostly Freud's various dogs — Lun-Yu, Jo-fi, Lun and Jumbo.

Felix Deutsch, Freud's medical doctor, at one time took care of Lun. He reported that Lun suffered a false pregnancy. 'Have you ever heard', he asked, 'of a dog with a false pregnancy? I am almost inclined to say: that can only happen to the dog of an analyst.'

The *pièce de résistance* of the display is the original analytic couch, which was brought to London when Freud moved here from Vienna. Behind it, also brought over from Vienna, is the chair in which Freud sat taking notes while his patient lay on the couch freely associating.

Gordon Museum

The Medical School, Guy's Hospital, St Thomas's Street, SE1 9RT
Tel: 071-955 5000, ext. 3037

Underground: London Bridge
Rail: London Bridge
Bus: 17, 21, 22A, 35, 40, 43, 47, 48, 133, 214, 344, 501, 505, 521, D1, D11, P3, P11
Car park (paying)

Opening times: Mon-Fri 9.00-17.00
Admission: only to visitors with medical or similar qualifications, arranged by prior
appointment with the Curator

Library: admission only by prior appointment and at the discretion of the Librarian
(071-955 4234)

Photography: allowed by prior permission

This is very much a teaching museum of the medical and dental schools at Guy's Hospital. It is in constant use during term times, although the arrangement is such that there can be lectures, demonstrations or tutorial groups in one part, while other parts are free. The interesting and very practical structure, which dates from 1905, consists of four inter-communicating quadrants, forming a square with a central spiral staircase. In each quadrant, two upper galleries contain pathology specimens. At the bottom level are teaching areas and objects of historical interest.

In the galleries, the specimens are grouped by organ, each provided with general comments and a detailed case history. Furthermore, a high proportion of these specimens are relatively recent examples, with good modern case evaluations.

Among the remarkable historical exhibits on the floor level of each quadrant, the most prized are the original specimens studied by, respectively, Hodgkin, Addison and Bright, which led to the recognition of the diseases named after these distinguished Guy's physicians.

Mention must also be made of the wax models, made by Joseph Towne between 1826 and 1879, of dissected cadavers and of dermatological disorders. However, although these give vivid impressions of diseased conditions, students are these days better served by the library of video demonstrations shown on the monitors provided.

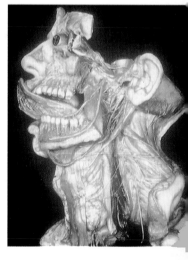

Wax model by Joseph Towne of a dissection to display the nerves and some blood vessels of the head and neck.

Horniman Museum and Gardens

100 London Road, Forest Hill, SE23 3PQ
Tel: 081-699 1872

Rail: Forest Hill
Bus: P4, 78, 176, 185, 312 (stop outside museum)
122, 171, 194, 194A, 63 (stop nearby)
Car parking (in nearby streets)

Opening times: Mon-Fri 10.30 - 17.30, Sun 14.00 - 17.30
Admission: free

Cafeteria
Library
Access for wheelchairs to most areas
Group visits: arrange with Education Officer, telephone ext. 124

The Horniman is an excellent small museum with a natural history collection well displayed on taxonomic lines, giving a clear account of the living world, very informative for students up to pre-university level. This collection reveals the anatomy and the interrelationships of the creatures classified, as well as giving some useful examples of evolutionary development. It also presents many stuffed and mounted specimens of birds and mammals including a spectacular large walrus which has awed visitors for nearly a century. And there are, in addition, a few typical fossils to show how evidence of evolution was assembled.

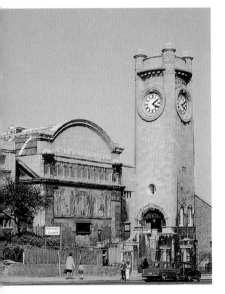

The only living things among the exhibits are the fish in a graceful aquarium arranged as a cascade from the first to the ground floor. It illustrates the various forms of freshwater life as a stream broadens into a river and then flows out to the sea, but also draws attention to current threats to the underwater environment. This small but imaginative display would be an asset to any museum in the world.

The museum's other riches are divided between an ethnographic collection and a collection of musical instruments of world renown. The collections have grown from those accumulated by Frederick Horniman at the end of the nineteenth century. At the beginning of the twentieth, he gave them to the citizens of London, together with the *art nouveau* building in which the museum is housed and the gardens beside that building.

The Horniman Museum.

The Imperial War Museum, formerly (1815-1930) the Bethlem Royal Hospital.

Imperial War Museum

Lambeth Road, SE1 6HZ
Tel: 071-416 5320

Underground: Lambeth North, Elephant and Castle
Rail: Waterloo
Bus: 1, 3, 12, 53, 59, 63, 68, 109, 159, 171, 184, 188, 344

Opening times: Daily 10.00 - 18.00
Admission: £££ (concessions)

Restaurant
Library
Access for wheelchairs
Group visits: telephone the Education Department (ext. 5312, 5313)

lthough the title of 'Imperial' may bring to mind wars in India, Africa and even
North America in previous centuries, the museum confines itself to wars in
which the United Kingdom was a participant in the twentieth century, with the
emphasis very much on the two World Wars. Furthermore, apart from a harrowing display of the Belsen concentration camp at the time when British troops liberated it in
1945 and a few German bombs, guns, and pieces of aeroplanes, the items on display are
mostly objects manufactured in Britain and the Commonwealth: weapons of war, military
and civilian uniforms, flags, commemorative crockery, films and recordings, and so on, as
well as letters and diaries and paintings by British war artists.

The interesting building in which the museum is housed was formerly (from 1815 to
1930) the Bethlem Royal Hospital, an institution for treatment of the insane (see p.15).
After fifty years as a museum laid out in conventional style, the Imperial War Museum
was the subject of a major redevelopment in 1989, and now presents to the public an
award-winning series of halls and smaller rooms in which the collections are displayed to
best advantage.

There is no doubt that, through the ages, wars have enlisted the skills of top-ranking
scientists and engineers. In the guns and planes and articles of subsidiary equipment to be

*Left: General view of the Museum galleries, showing,
among other exhibits, the Spitfire and Fockewolf fighter
planes and a V2 rocket.*

*Below: An air-raid warden's post from the 'Blitz
Experience' exhibition, recreating in objects, sound and
pictures an impression of life in London during the bombing
of 1940-1941.*

seen in the museum, the precision of the workmanship and the intricacy of the design are obvious at a glance. The guns on display are labelled with much technical data — manufacturer, date, calibre, range, theatre of operation, etc. — and a number of interactive video displays give further details of the use and deployment of the weapons. Equally, the various items of medical application and the exhibits relating to communications, photography, signalling, etc., all involve a high level of science and technology.

However, the rows of machine guns, rifles and pistols in the display cabinets or the field guns, anti-aircraft guns, mortars and rockets standing among the tanks and aeroplanes freely accessible out in the main hall evoke a mixed reaction. Their mass-produced lethality has replaced the beautiful decorations on the hand-made weapons of previous centuries; their manufacture swallowed up a large fraction of the nation's wealth; yet their use twice saved the country from defeat in war against Germany.

The military material in the museum's displays are the products of the highest-quality engineering but may seem to some visitors to be encased in an aura of bleakness. However, this should not be allowed to deter those visitors from seeing the remarkable art collection. Many major British twentieth-century artists are represented by war-time or immediately post-war works. These show military life and action, infliction of damage and receipt of medical attention, manufacture of ships and munitions, the land seen from a bomber's cockpit or the bombers seen from the land beneath, and the wars seen through civilians' eyes. Uniformly these works depict the horror and misery of war.

Furthermore, the museum has reference departments dealing with documents, sound and film recordings, photographs, and books as well as with the materials of the collections on display. Some sections of this reference material are unrivalled in the world, although prior arrangement with the Curators is necessary for anyone who wishes to consult them.

The Enigma Decoding Machine used by the German Naval Command during the 1939-1945 War. Alan Turing and others were able to build a British version of the machine, allowing coded German signals to be deciphered.

Kew Bridge Steam Museum

Green Dragon Lane, Brentford, Middlesex TW8 0EN
Tel: 081-568 4757

Underground: Gunnersbury or South Ealing, then bus
Rail: Kew Bridge
Bus: 65, 237, 267, 391 (and 7 on Sundays)
Car park (free)

Opening times: Daily 11.00-17.00, but engines run only on Saturdays, Sundays and Bank
Holiday Mondays
Admission: ££ (concessions)
Restaurant
Limited access for wheelchairs
Group visits: write to or telephone the Assistant Curator

The museum, established in 1975, is owned by and officially named the Kew Bridge Engine Trust and Water Supply Museum Ltd. Displays to illustrate the development of the supply of pure drinking water to the public are being developed. But meanwhile, so much steam hisses from the old pumping engines on show that the name of the museum has been changed in most publications.

There are many very large engines to be seen. This means engines up to four stories high and with cylinders up to 100 inches (250 cm) in diameter. Note, however, that the engines are set going only on Saturdays, Sundays, and Bank Holiday Mondays (except by special arrangement with the General Manager); each runs for about 30 minutes two or three times a day, but in a visit of an hour or so one can see most of the engines in action and, furthermore, climb up alongside them, watch the vast rocking beams and walk in amongst the connecting rods as they move up and down.

A view of the end of the beam of 'Grand Junction 90', the world's largest working beam engine, built in 1846 with a cylinder 90 inches in diameter.

Kirkaldy Testing Museum

99 Southwark Street, SE1 0JF
Tel: 0322 332195 (Curator)

Underground: Blackfriars, Waterloo, London Bridge
Rail: Blackfriars, Waterloo, London Bridge
Bus: 17, 21, 22A, 35, 40, 43, 45, 47, 48, 59, 63, 133, 149, 172, 214, 344, 501, 505, 521, D1, P11

Opening times: by appointment with the Curator
Admission: ££
Library
Group visits: write to or telephone the Curator

In 1865 David Kirkaldy came to London from Scotland, having been employed in Glasgow as an engineer for nearly twenty years. He set up, in Southwark, a vast machine, just under 15 m long, 'for the purpose of testing all kinds of constructive materials, and that under various stresses, namely, Pulling, Thrusting, Bending, Twisting, Shearing, Punching and Bulging.'

The machine is still there as the centrepiece of this museum, along with other devices for testing the strength of concrete, of chains, of steel plate, and so on. Over the years, Kirkaldy's was called on to test the strength of the girders of the Tay Bridge and pieces from the Comet aircraft, in both cases after the disasters, and girders of the Sydney Harbour Bridge, to check that there would be no Australian disaster.

There is astonishing evidence here of the quality of Victorian engineering, lovingly preserved by a group of industrial archaeology enthusiasts.

David Kirkaldy (1820-1897)

Livesey Museum

682 Old Kent Road, SE15 1JF
Tel: 071-639 5604

Underground: Elephant and Castle (and then bus 53, 141 or 177), New Cross
(and then bus 21)
Rail: Queen's Road (and then bus 21, 53, 78, 141 or 177)
Bus: 21, 53, 78, 141 or 177
Car parking in nearby streets

Opening times: Mon-Sat 10.00 - 17.00
Admission: free

Ground floor access for wheelchairs
Photography: allowed, but not for publication
Group visits: write to or telephone the Director

The museum, housed in a decorative Victorian building, formerly a public library, is the exhibition hall of Southwark Borough Council's Cuming Museum. Small but lively exhibitions, usually dealing with a specific scientific or technological subject, are mounted for periods of about six months. Recent exhibitions have dealt with sound, the physics of light, environmental pollution, and similar topics. Explanations of the exhibits are not detailed, but encourage participation by young children.

The enthusiasm of the young visitors to the museum shows how successfully the museum staff fulfil their programme. Usually, the exhibitions are designed to tie in with the National Curriculum used by schools. (Intending visitors should always telephone beforehand to find out about the current display.)

Above: Leaflet for the 'Use Your Loaf' exhibition.

Right: Young visitors absorbed in an experiment.

London Butterfly House

Syon Park, Brentford TW8 8JF
Tel: 081-560 7272

Underground: Gunnersbury, then bus
Rail: Brentford, Syon Lane
Bus: 116, 117, 237, 267, E2, E8
Car park *(free)*

Opening times: daily, summer 10.00-17.00, winter 10.00-16.00
Admission: ££ (concessions)

Access for wheelchairs
Group visits: write to or telephone the Manager

Brightly coloured individuals from a couple of dozen species of butterflies and moths flutter elegantly around the warm and humid indoor garden of the Butterfly House. There are approximately 100,000 species of butterflies and moths in the world, so only a minute proportion is on view.

The representatives of those to be seen are very decorative, and many have wings with spans of 8 to 10 centimetres. You can also see them feeding, resting and (according to the brochure) courting. A glass-fronted box allows sight of a few hundred chrysales and occasionally, over a period of an hour or two, a butterfly emerges from one. A few other vivaria contain a variety of insects.

It is a very quiet place and nothing much happens in the half hour or so that you might reasonably spend there. It would be sensible to combine a visit here with a visit either to the Kew Bridge Steam Museum (see p.44) or to Syon House, adjacent to the Butterfly House.

A butterfly of the species Phoebis sennae.

London Canal Museum

12-13 New Wharf Road, N1 9RT
Tel: 071-713 0836

Underground: King's Cross
Rail: King's Cross, St Pancras
Bus: 10, 14, 14A, 17, 18, 30, 45, 46, 63, 73, 74, 214, 221, 259, C12
Car parking on side roads at weekends

Opening times: Tue-Sun 10.00-16.30
Admission: ££

Library
Access for wheelchairs to ground floor only
Group visits: by prior arrangement by letter or telephone to the Manager

From 1850 to the 1900s ice was imported by ship from Norway to the London docks and thence by barge to the old warehouse, alongside the Battlebridge Basin of the Regent's Canal, in which the museum is now housed. The museum was opened in the Spring of 1992 and has exhibits relating to canals, boats and barges, including a reconstructed narrowboat. Diagrams and old pictures give a brief account of the excavation of the Regent's Canal.

Other pictures illustrate the work and customs of the boatpeople who carried goods along it and there are a few artefacts of the boatpeople and their families. Video films contrast a present canal trip with one in 1924. And there are the remarkable remains, accessed by a ramp from the ground floor to the first floor, of stalls in the stable which used to form a sort of horse hotel for the animals that pulled the ice carts.

Beneath the building there are two vast wells, 10 m in diameter, dug into the London clay, in which blocks of ice were stored. Former offices in the building have been converted for lecture and classroom use.

The London Canal Museum from the Basin, with visiting boats.

London Fire Brigade Museum

Winchester House, 94a Southwark Bridge Road, SE1 0EG
Tel: 071-587 2894

Underground: Borough
Rail: London Bridge
Bus: 344

Opening times: Mon-Fri 10.00-16.00
Admission: free but only by prior appointment with the Curator

Group visits: telephone the Curator

Londoners learned a lesson in 1666 when 13,200 houses, 87 parish churches, and St Paul's Cathedral were lost in the Great Fire. Arrangements then began for organized fire-fighting. However, it was not until 1866 that a formal Metropolitan Fire Brigade was established. Twelve years later, its headquarters were moved to the building, erected in 1820, that now houses the museum and after various administrative re-arrangements the service became the present London Fire Brigade.

Winchester House, Southwark Bridge Road, home and workplace to London's Chief Fire Officers from 1878 to 1937 and now housing the museum.

The museum's exhibits cover three and a quarter centuries of fire-fighting and show how the technology has progressed from simple hand-operated stirrup pumps to the powered pumps of the present, how the conveyances have changed from the unadorned water-tanks on wheels to horse-drawn vehicles to modern engines, and how the firemen's clothing has changed from smocks in the colours of insurance companies to the efficient present-day wear, which can be supplemented by breathing apparatus run on compressed air. And the bravery of firefighters over the centuries is attested by the medals and other mementoes on display here.

London Gas Museum

British Gas plc (North Thames), Twelvetrees Crescent, E3 3JH
Tel: 071-987 2000, ext. 3344

Underground: Bromley-by-Bow
Rail: Devons Road (Docklands Light Railway)
Bus: 86, 108, 278, S2 (to Bromley-by-Bow station);
8, 10, 25, 225 (to Bow Road); 276 (to Manor Road)
Car park (free)

Opening times: Mon-Fri 9.30-16.00
Admission: free but only by prior appointment with the Curator

Restaurant (staff restaurant, open 12.00-14.00)
Library
Group visits: write to or telephone the Curator
Photography: allowed, except of certain installations

You don't expect to find a museum in the middle of a major industrial site, but that is the situation imaginatively created by British Gas, North Thames, at its Bromley-by-Bow works. The museum provides clear and well-explained accounts of the technology of the industry, from the early methods of manufacturing gas by the cooking of coal to present-day extraction of methane gas from fields in the North Sea. But production of the raw gas is only the first stage of a process that also requires purification and distribution, as well as utilization of the chemical by-products, all of which are well illustrated here.

In the first-floor rooms of the museum, the civil and domestic applications of gas are enthusiastically demonstrated: street lighting, former theatre and home lighting, home cooking and heating, and even an astonishing gas-powered radio. In addition, the museum provides a detailed history of British commercial gas production, from the time of the Gas Light and Coke Company, the world's first commercial producer of gas, established in 1810, through nationalization and back to the present arrangement of private ownership.

The London Gas Museum.

The London Planetarium.

London Planetarium (and Madame Tussaud's)

Marylebone Road, NW1 5LR
Tel: 071-935 6861

Underground: Baker Street
Rail: Baker Street
Bus: 2A, 2B, 13, 18, 27, 74, 113, 139, 159, 274

Opening times: April-September, daily 10.00-18.00
October-March, daily 10.00-17.30

Admission: £££ (concessions)

Restaurant
Group visits: write to or telephone the Group Booking Office
(071-486 1121)

The Planetarium offers a science-based display and the Space Trail exhibition that acts as an introduction to it offers the same and more information, though in a different medium and with interactive video. The presentation in the Planetarium is of popular astronomy aimed at all ages from 11 upwards. With such a wide age range in its intended audience, the scientific ideas presented in the show are inevitably not more difficult than one might expect to find in a typical schools television documentary on the solar system or the galaxies or star formation. The visitors — a large proportion of whom are children — seem to be fully absorbed by what is shown to them.

The Planetarium offers special educational programmes, each designed for a particular age group. These are intended to complement the National Science Curriculum. Details can be arranged with the Planetarium staff by teachers arranging school group visits. Also, there is a special 'Sky This Month' presentation at 5 p.m. on the first Wednesday of each month, followed by audience questions.

Left: The Space Trail exhibition hall.

Below: The Zeiss Projector, producing an image of the Earth as seen from the Moon.

That the Planetarium is a subsidiary of the waxworks is evidenced by wax figures of Galileo, Halley, and Einstein (who sits mournfully considering the equation $E = mc^2$); and there is a symbolic statue celebrating Copernicus. In the Madame Tussaud's galleries there are just two figures of scientific interest: Sir Christopher Wren (a former professor of astronomy) who is shown twiddling a pair of compasses as he contemplates rebuilding St Paul's Cathedral; and Benjamin Franklin, considered only as an ambassador of the rebellious North American states.

London Transport Museum

Covent Garden, WC2E 7BB
Tel: 071-379 6344

Underground: Covent Garden, Charing Cross, Leicester Square
Rail: Charing Cross
Bus: 1, 6, 9, 11, 13, 15, 23, 26, 68, 76, 77A, 168, 171, 171A, 176, 188, 505

Opening times: daily 10.00-18.00
Admission: £££ (concessions)

Cafeteria
Information centre (Library, admission only by prior appointment)
Access for wheelchairs
Group visits: write to or telephone the Group Visits Service

Entrance to the London Transport Museum.

A recent complete redesign and refurbishment of this museum allows a clear presentation of the story of one of the world's most celebrated transport systems. On display is a large collection of buses, trams, trolleybuses and underground trains which have been used by London Transport and its predecessors.

London Transport itself is the successor to a number of earlier organizations which were brought together about 60 years ago. However, public transport had been available to Londoners for 100 years before then. A considerable part of the museum is given over

to tracing the history of transportation in London, from early horse-drawn omnibuses, confined to the centre of the city, to the present system serving an area of about 2,000 square miles (5,000 sq km).

The information is presented through thematic key exhibit areas with working models and interactive videos. Displays explore topics such as the evolution of the bus, the growth of London, and how the development of London's transport affected the growth of the capital and people's lives.

The museum is housed in the Victorian building that was formerly the flower market. The recent work has created attractive galleries, shop, cafeteria, information centre, etc., within this interesting iron and glass structure.

Above: In the foreground a London B-type bus of 1911, behind it a horse-drawn Thomas Tilling knifeboard bus of about 1875, and trams in the rear.

Left: A Metropolitan Railway engine, M23, built in 1866 and used on the Inner Circle (now the Circle Line); behind it, a 1938 Tube Stock standard underground driving car.

A *black rhinoceros.*

London Zoo

Regent's Park, NW1 4RY
Tel: 071-722 3333

Underground: Camden Town, Regent's Park
Rail: Marylebone
Bus: Z1 (to main gate, summer only); 274 (to Ormonde Terrace) C2 (to Gloucester Gate)
Car park (paying); Street parking (free)

Opening times:1 March-31 Oct daily 10.00-17.30 (last admission 16.30)
1 Nov-28 Feb daily 10.00-16.00 (last admission 15.00)
Admission: £££ (concessions)

Restaurants
Library: admission only to research workers by prior arrangement
Access for wheelchairs
Nursing room; changing room for babies; playground with roundabouts,
rocking horses, etc.; animal rides
Group visits: schools should contact the Education Department (ext. 551);
others should contact the Group Sales Department (ext. 235)

L ondon Zoo, originally the Gardens of the Zoological Society of London, was established in 1828 and is older than all other modern zoological gardens and displays except that of Paris. For over 150 years it has been one of the most popular attractions of London, for natives and tourists alike. Nevertheless it came close to extinction in the late 1980s. Fortunately, a combination of enterprising new direction and generous donations allowed a rescue plan to be put into action in 1993. In consequence, although the long-term future of London Zoo is not yet absolutely assured, its continued existence is now very probable.

People go to zoos to look at animals and those on display at London Zoo are now to be seen to far better advantage than at any time in the past. The conditions in the Regent's Park zoo have been greatly improved in the past 20 years. To see animals living in the environment of a wild life park, though, you still have to travel from London to the Zoo's outstation at Whipsnade.

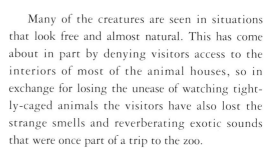

Right: Lubetkin's Penguin Pool.

Below: A Humbolt Penguin chick.

Many of the creatures are seen in situations that look free and almost natural. This has come about in part by denying visitors access to the interiors of most of the animal houses, so in exchange for losing the unease of watching tightly-caged animals the visitors have also lost the strange smells and reverberating exotic sounds that were once part of a trip to the zoo.

The number of species on display is not large — about 650 in all, although represented by a total of about 12,000 living creatures — but they give a fair representation of the variety of animal life and form. The choice of new additions to the collection of animals now favours endangered species, to tie in with the research programme of the Institute of

Zoology, a constituent unit of the University of London, which is housed within the confines of the Zoological Society's gardens.

This programme gives particular attention to conservation problems and to breeding techniques for use with captive animals, often in collaboration with other centres and zoos, in the U.K. and abroad. There is not much spectator-appeal in some of the species studied in this manner — for example, *Partula* snails and Wartbiter crickets — but others, such as Asian lions, Sumatran tigers, and Golden Lion tamarins, provide the exciting sights for which the visitors have come and the interesting memories that they want to take home with them.

In the century and a half of its existence, the London Zoo has been the site of many significant buildings and the improved viewing conditions provided in the last two decades have been arranged by the erection of important new houses, or the substantial modification of existing ones. An unchanged structure is Lubetkin's much-loved graceful penguin pool.

Spider Encounter: young visitors are introduced by a keeper to one of the Zoo's denizens.

This has been joined by Snowdon's spectacular walk-through aviary, a new elephant house, a charming new small mammal house which also contains, in its basement, a dimly-lit gallery for viewing nocturnal animals, and several other new buildings. Only the aquarium remains in the more-or-less unchanged old style, but it, too, is due for refurbishment within the next few years.

A money's-worth visit to London Zoo requires at least half a day and involves considerable walking about. To relieve feet and hunger pains there are several restaurants, cafeterias and ice-cream stalls. There are many arrangements especially for children: a Children's Zoo area, animal rides, and animal presentations, usually with an educational slant, by the keepers. Other daily events are of equal delight to children and adults, including animal feeding (particularly lions and penguins), elephant weighing and washing, and shows of other animals in action.

Metropolitan Police Crime Museum

New Scotland Yard, 8-10 Broadway, SW1H 0BG

Underground: St James's Park
Rail: Victoria
Bus: 11, 24, 88, 511

Opening times: guided tours only (approx. 10.30 and 14.30)
Admission: all intending visitors should apply by letter to the Curator. Preference is given to those involved in work connected with the police, e.g. magistrates and others involved in maintaining law and order. People working in forensic science and allied subjects may be admitted at the discretion of the Curator.

Access for wheelchairs
Photography: not allowed
Group visits: write to the Curator

This museum, established in 1874, is the oldest police museum in the world specifically limited to crime. On display are implements of mischief of every sort: tools for burglary, robbery, forgery, drug smuggling, poisoning, spying, terrorism and murder. Nearly every item in the collection has a book-length story behind it and

The corner of the Museum devoted to recent crimes of violence.

the Curator will gladly discourse on any of them until time runs out. Most of the exhibits relate to crimes that ended in capture and conviction of the criminal and in most of the recent cases the success depended on applications of forensic science.

The range of these applications is remarkably wide. It includes recovery of fingerprints from old cloth or paper, analysis of ash or incrustations after attempts to burn or boil away evidence, reconstruction of skulls from the fragments into which they had been shattered, tracking bullet paths through flesh, elemental determinations of tooth fillings, and many other examples of the craft of the forensic laboratories.

Museum of Artillery at the Rotunda

Repository Road, SE18 4DN
Tel: 081-854 2242

Rail: Woolwich Arsenal; Woolwich Dockyard
Bus: 89, 122, 161, 161A, 178, 469
Car park (free)

Opening times: 1 November - 31 March: Mon-Fri 12.00-16.00 Sat-Sun 13.00-16.00
1 April - 31 October: Mon-Fri 12.00-17.00 Sat-Sun 13.00-17.00
Admission: free

Access for wheelchairs
Group visits: contact the Curator (081-316 5402)
Photography: allowed only for private purposes

This startling museum, rarely advertised and situated on the edge of a Ministry of Defence complex of military barracks, hospital and training ground, is housed in an architectural gem. The Rotunda is a Georgian building by Nash, based on the design of a large tent or marquee but constructed with brick walls and a lead roof.

Within and around the Rotunda are cannon, mortars, and many other types of ordnance, of all shapes and sizes, and ranging in age from a late fourteenth-century bombard, which may have been of the type used at the Battle of Crécy, to modern rocket-launching devices. The development of manufacturing technology and the steady improvement of weapon design can be clearly followed.

There is on display an interesting collection of small arms and other weapons such as Gatling and Maxim machine guns, rampart guns, and hand mortars. In addition, there are ornamental cannon (including a handsome 'dragon gun' from Burma) and the ceremonial guns used at state funerals. The collection includes a wide variety of artillery ammunition and a splendid array of models.

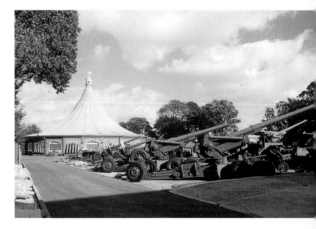

A view of the Rotunda, with, to the left, cannon from the sixteenth to the eighteenth century and, to the right, modern artillery from the 1940s to the present.

Museum of Garden History

St Mary-at-Lambeth, Lambeth Palace Road, SE1 7JU
Tel: 071-261 1891

Underground: Lambeth North, Waterloo, Westminster
Rail: Waterloo, Charing Cross, Victoria
Bus: 3, 77, 159, 344, 507
Car parking (Sundays only)

Opening times: from first Sunday in March to second Sunday in December:
Mon-Fri 11.00-15.00; Sun 10.30-17.00
Admission: free but donations welcome

Cafeteria
Access for wheelchairs
Group visits: write to or telephone the Director
Photography: allowed for a small fee

The museum is housed in St Mary's Church, the former parish church of Lambeth, near to the site of the nursery that John Tradescant, the plant collector and gardener, established in the seventeenth century. The museum displays a limited collection of early garden design, a few early books on gardening and some horticultural implements of the nineteenth and early twentieth centuries.

At the back of the church, the former churchyard has been converted to a charming garden in seventeenth-century style; but the tomb of John Tradescant has been left in place, and also that of Rear-Admiral William Bligh, he of the Mutiny on the *Bounty*, and also an explorer, botanist and Fellow of the Royal Society (see p.207). Another FRS buried in St Mary's Church is Elias Ashmole, who was an enthusiastic seventeenth-century amateur astronomer as well as the founder of the Ashmolean Museum in Oxford.

A garden in the style of the seventeenth century, created behind the Museum in part of St Mary's Churchyard.

Museum of London

London Wall, EC2Y 5HN
Tel: 071-600 3699

Underground: Barbican, St Paul's, Moorgate, Bank
Rail: Moorgate, St Paul's Thameslink, Cannon Street
Bus: 4, 172, 279a (to Museum of London) 8, 11, 15, 22b, 23, 25, 26, 501 (to St Paul's)

Opening times: Tue-Sat, Bank Holidays 10.00-18.00, Sun 12.00-18.00
Admission: ££ (concessions and free after 16.30)

Restaurant immediately outside
Library: admission only by prior appointment
Access for wheelchairs
Photography: allowed, but only without tripods
Group visits: write to the Education Department

A museum devoted to the history of London and its immediate environs over the past 3,000 years inevitably contains some items touching the scientific, medical and engineering professions. But there is not much of such material in this light and airy and attractively laid-out museum.

Examples of the application of technology to warfare have been so numerous through the ages that there is always the probability of a few pieces surviving, whatever the catastrophe. So here we find items of weaponry from prehistoric inhabitants, from Roman occupiers, from Anglo-Saxons, and from the Normans, all of whom combined to produce the present-day population of the city. There are also other relics of wars, from Tudor soldiers' guns and swords to twentieth-century civilians' gas masks.

Most of the museum's exhibits relate to domestic life and the city's commerce. Into the first, sickness was always likely to intrude; items displayed include some relating to the Great Plague (Black Death) of 1348-1349 and also a few examples of the instruments of surgeons and apothecaries down the centuries. Commerce regularly harnessed technology to increase profit and items of London transport, manufacturing practices, and communication by post, telephone and radio are displayed.

The museum is housed in a building constructed around a square in which a restful nursery garden has been established. This shows, in more or less historical order, the plants purveyed to Londoners through the centuries, together with the names and dates of the gardeners and nurserymen who introduced them.

A bucket and fire squirt marked 'Aldgate Ward 1672'. required parish fire-fighting equipment after the Great Fire.

Museum of Mankind

6 Burlington Gardens, W1X 2EX
Tel: 071-437 2224; 071-323 8043 (Information Office)

Underground: Green Park, Piccadilly Circus, Oxford Circus
Rail: Victoria, Waterloo
Bus: 3, 6, 12, 13, 15, 53, 88, 94, 159 to Regent Street; 9, 14, 19, 22, 38 to Piccadilly;
25 to New Bond Street or Berkeley Street

Opening times: Mon-Sat 10.00-17.00, Sun 14.30-18.00
Admission: free

Cafeteria
Library: admission only by Reader's Ticket
Access for wheelchairs
Group visits: write to or telephone the Information Officer

This relatively small museum is the temporary display venue (now in its twenty-third year) of the enormous ethnographic collection of the British Museum. Only a small fraction of the collection can be shown at any time, so the displays are changed periodically. At any one time, you can expect to find here examples of the technology, expressed in weapons and tools, of peoples culturally remote from the scientific societies of the Western world, even though they are often of this century. Accompanying displays give an idea of the beliefs of the societies exhibited. In some instances the displays include objects used for medical purposes or objects that are claimed to assist divination.

The Victorian building that houses the museum was erected in 1866 as administrative offices for the University of London. Its use then transferred to the Civil Service at the beginning of this century and to the British Museum in 1970. The façade in Burlington Gardens contains statues representing leading thinkers throughout history, including many of the most distinguished scientists and physicians, among whom are Aristotle, Davy, Galen, Galileo, Harvey, Hunter, Laplace, Leibnitz and Newton.

*A contemporary Mexican papier mâché display.
The Apocalypse. for the Day of the Dead.*

Museum of the Moving Image

South Bank, Waterloo, SE1 8XT
Tel: 071-928 3535

Underground: Waterloo, Embankment
Rail: Waterloo, Charing Cross
Bus: 1, 15, 68, 76, 77, 168, 171, 171A, 176, P11
Car park (paying, South Bank car parks)

Opening times: Daily 10.00-18.00 (last admissions 17.00)
Admission: £££ (concessions)

Restaurant (by riverside entrance outside museum)
Access for wheelchairs
Photography: allowed, but no tripods
Group visits: contact Group Bookings Officer (071-815 1350)

Cinema and television are especially characteristic technologies of the twentieth century and MOMI (Museum of the Moving Image, a division of the British Film Institute) provides a series of informative displays about both. In the few years since it opened in 1988, the museum has become extremely popular, attracting, on average, half a million visitors each year. Part of the attraction is undoubtedly the space given

The Control Centre which organizes the programmes displayed on the seventy independent monitor screens in the Museum.

to memorabilia of stars of the film and electronic screens. There are also sequences from new and old films and TV shows to be seen on innumerable screens and television monitor tubes scattered through the forty-four display areas. However, a considerable amount of technical information is also presented.

There is a particularly good presentation of the precursors of the cinema — early devices that managed to make images move, with opaque names like zoetrope, thaumatrope and phenakistascope. Although in these cases the images are very limited and the movements very simple and repetitive, a special pleasure comes from seeing them still in action and in being able to comprehend how they work, because all is open to view.

Further exhibits do indeed explain how a cinema projector works and one can even see clips from the original Lumière brothers' films. But within a few years of the Lumières' developments, trickeries ('special effects') were introduced into cinematography. Many displays show clearly how the tricks were effected: how cameras zoom, how monsters are made to roam cities, how people can be made to appear against dangerous or impossible backgrounds, etc. But the producers became, at the same time, so adroit that, even though the mechanics of the tricks are known, the moving image on the screen is still able to deceive.

Television is presented with an interesting account of its historical development, but little mention is made of its technology. Nothing is said, for example, of the differences between the British, North American and Continental colour transmission systems (PAL, NCVS and SECAM), which frustrate so many tourists each year. However, modern electronic technology plays its part in providing the signals for the seventy monitor and demonstration screens situated in the forty-four exhibition areas of the museum. The signals come from the Control Centre (itself a display feature of the museum) equipped with laser discs, allowing a thousand different video sequences to be shown continuously, each one under computer control.

The museum brochure advises that two hours should be allowed for a visit; rather less is required if you don't wish to spend much time looking at exhibits dealing with former film stars, rather more if you wish to watch all the film extracts right through. Children might wish to spend a much longer time, since there are facilities for them to make their own animated movies.

The 'Temple to the Gods', a gallery glorifying actors of the era of silent films.

National Army Museum

Royal Hospital Road, Chelsea, SW3 4HT
Tel: 071-730 0717

Underground: Sloane Square, South Kensington
Rail: Victoria (then by bus)
Bus: 239 (not Sunday) to Royal Hospital Rd; 11, 19, or 22 to King's Road (Smith Street);
137 to Pimlico Road
Car park, but priority (by prior arrangement) for the incapacitated

Opening times: daily 10.00-17.30 (closed 1 Jan, Mayday Bank Holiday, 24-26 Dec)
Admission: free

Cafeteria
Library: admission only with Reader's Ticket, obtained by prior application to the
Librarian
Access for wheelchairs
Group visits: by prior arrangement with the Education Officer
(talks on scientific aspects of the collections can be arranged)
Photography: only with a Permit, costing £1

The museum provides a well-presented display of the development of small arms from the sixteenth century to the present times. The weapons galleries are arranged in a chronological order. Clear explanations are given of the technology of the early weapons — arquebuses, matchlocks, flintlocks, and other types of musket — which in turn leads to more modern types of fire-arm.

There is a substantial collection of all these weapons, allowing their evolution to be appreciated. Also on display are various rangefinders, signalling devices, instruments used for medical treatment, etc. However, these displays occupy only a part of the museum. The remainder is given over to uniforms, medals, dioramas, portraits of soldiers, paintings of battles, and miscellaneous military objects, all of considerable historical, but of limited scientific or technological interest.

A display in the Weapons Gallery, showing soldiers manning an urban defence post in Ulster, circa 1972.

Aerial view of the Greenwich site. The group of buildings on the left form the Royal Naval College, lying between the river and the Queen's House, to the right of which is the National Maritime Museum.

National Maritime Museum

Greenwich, SE10 9NF
Tel: 081-858 4422

River: from Westminster, Charing Cross, Tower, or Thames Barrier Piers
Rail: Greenwich, Maze Hill; (Docklands Light Railway to Island Gardens
and then by foot-tunnel beneath the Thames)
Bus: 53, 53X, 177, 180, 286
Limited street car parking

Opening times: April-September, Mon-Sat 10.00-18.00, Sun 12.00-18.00 October-March:
Mon-Sat 10.00-17.00, Sun 14.00-17.00
Admission: £££ (concessions and 'passport' ticket)

Restaurant
Library: Reader's Ticket required
Access for wheelchairs
Group visits: contact Education Department (081-312 6608)
or Visitor Services Manager (081-312 6603)

One of the videos available in the Education Programmes that can be arranged for school groups at the National Maritime Museum is *The Sea and Science*. In a real sense, most aspects of mankind's developing mastery of sea travel have gone hand in hand with developments of science and technology. The mere ability to put to sea in a vessel without immediately sinking has been gained by a series of technological triumphs over several thousand years.

Apart from ship-building, it is clear that powering the movements of ships at sea (by oar, sail, steam, oil or nuclear reactions), navigation, naval warfare, and oceanographic studies all tie maritime history closely with engineering and science. So a large fraction of the exhibits in this attractively displayed and elegantly housed museum will hold the attention of all those with an interest in the history of both pure and applied (that is, technological) science.

Indeed, maritime technology has such a long history that it begins, as it were, to turn round and bite its own tail. A very interesting display in Gallery 10 deals with the techniques of maritime archaeology. It is shown how these, together with complicated applications of wood chemistry, are being used to conserve the waterlogged wood of ancient vessels, up to 2,500 years old, retrieved in recent years from mud and silt around European coasts. It is also shown how to interpret the finds so as to

Above: Dolphin Sundial. *designed by Christopher Daniel in 1977 to celebrate Her Majesty the Queen's Silver Jubilee and sculpted by Edwin Russell.*

Left: Captain James Cook. *oil on canvas. by Nathaniel Dance.*

understand the technological methods by which the boats were constructed.

A particular glory of the museum is its collection of model ships. This collection has its origin in the requirements, in Britain, of the Lords of the Admiralty from the mid-seventeenth century onwards. These proposed that new ships for service in the Royal Navy be offered as precise scale models for their lordships to examine before deciding whether to proceed with the construction. The Navy kept the models until the creation of the National Maritime Museum in 1934. The models offer an unrivalled insight into the detailed design of all types of sea-going vessels. Most of the models are displayed in Gallery 3 but some are to be found in other galleries.

Many galleries — particularly Galleries 1, 5 and 6 — display navigational aids. As well as charts and globes, these range from sixteenth-century astrolabes and quadrants, and seventeenth-century telescopes, to modern electronic devices. Such instruments show with particular clarity the contributions of science to seamanship.

Seamanship and science combine in an exceptionally interesting way in Gallery 4, which is devoted to Captain James Cook and his expeditions to the southern Pacific and Australasia. Accounts are given of the observation of the Transit of Venus in 1769 by Charles Green, the astronomer of the party, and of the botanical work of Cook and Joseph Banks, the chief scientist aboard, as well as of Cook's cartography and his discovery of the land dispositions in the southern seas. The display includes many fine scientific instruments of the mid-eighteenth century and also portraits and marble busts of Cook, Banks (later President of the Royal Society) and others.

The Effects of a Heavy Lurch, *cartoon (1818) by George Cruikshank.*

Stamp to commemorate the bicentenary in 1991 of the birth of Charles Babbage,
inventor of mechanical calculators and computers.

National Postal Museum

London Chief Post Office, King Edward Street, EC1A 1LP
Tel: 071-239 5420

Underground: St Paul's, Barbican
Rail: Cannon Street, City (Thameslink)
Bus: 4, 8, 22, 22B, 25, 141, 501, 502, 509;
or 9, 11, 15, 15A (to Ludgate Hill)

Opening times: Mon-Fri 9.30-16.30
Admission: free

Group visits: write to the Manager

N ot unexpectedly, the National Postal Museum, though small, houses the defini-
tive collection of British postage stamps in all their issues and shades of colour.
Displays show the process of stamp production, letter-weighing and franking
machines, models of old mail coaches, and modern mail delivery systems.

The stamps on view include the philatelic depiction of scientists and science. Until
1965, most British stamps showed only the head of the monarch. Thereafter, to publicize
Britain and British achievements (and also because profit was to be made from frequently-
altered designs, first-day covers and the other collectables of philatelists), designs became
more adventurous. Scientists, engineers and medical practitioners began to be seen on the
envelopes of the letters crossing the kingdom. Lister was the first (1966) and others
include Florence Nightingale and Sir William Herschel (1969), Darwin (1982), Newton
(1987), and Babbage, Faraday, Watson-Watt and Whittle (1991). Stamps have also been
the vehicles of celebrating British engineering achievements, scientific societies, famous
centres like Kew, and the wildlife — animal and vegetable — of the kingdom.

The museum also contains a substantial
collection of stamps from countries of the
Commonwealth, as well as good though incomplete
collections from other countries. All these have their
own birds, flowers, fish, butterflies, and so on, as
well as their distinguished scholars; so their stamps,
too, have often displayed images of interest to
scientists, physicians and engineers.

*Some of the set of stamps issued in 1987 to mark the
tercentenary of the publication of Newton's book*
Philosophiae Naturalis Principia Mathematica.
presenting his theory of gravity.

A life-size model of a blue whale (Balaenoptera musculus). *on display in the Mammals Gallery of the Museum.*

Natural History Museum

Cromwell Road, SW7 5BD
Tel: 071-938 9123; 0426 927654 (recorded information); 071-938 9191 (Library)

Underground: South Kensington
Bus: 9, 10, 14, 30, 33, 45, 49, 52, 52A, 74, 503, C1

Opening times: Mon-Sat 10.00-17.50, Sun 11.00-17.50,
Admission: £££ (concessions)

Restaurant
Library: admission only by prior arrangement
Access for wheelchairs
Group visits: write to or telephone the Education Office

The Natural History Museum is top-ranking in every respect: in the magnitude of its collections (about 67 million items in all), in its size (20,000 m² of publicly accessible galleries, apart from the libraries and research areas); in the number of visitors it attracts (1.7 million a year); and in the quality of research carried out by its staff

An early watercolour of one of the galleries designed by Alfred Waterhouse, the architect of the Museum.

(including 350 scientific research workers). The overwhelming quality of the museum can be appreciated in the first sight one obtains of it from Cromwell Road: the immense façade of an intricate neo-Gothic design, with an improbable buff and blue terracotta facing, created by the architect Alfred Waterhouse in the 1870s. (An illuminating book about the building, *Alfred Waterhouse and the Natural History Museum* by Mark Girouard, Natural History Museum Publications, 1981, can usually be obtained from one of the Museum shops.)

The Museum's collections originally formed the Natural History section of the British Museum and these in turn had been developed from the collections amassed by Sir Hans Sloane and Sir Joseph Banks. At the British Museum the collections were in the care of four curators — of zoology, botany, geology and mineralogy — and in 1856 the distinguished comparative anatomist Richard Owen was appointed over them as Superintendent of the Natural History Departments.

Owen was the driving force behind the move to house the departments in a special

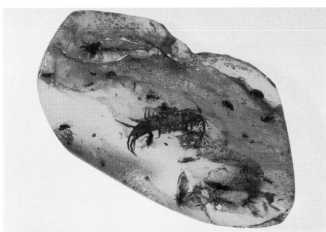

Above: An animated three-quarter scale model of maiasaura, with nest and young.

Left: An Eocene centipede, trapped in amber about fifty million years ago.

building of their own. The final floor plan of the Museum contained most of the essential features that Owen had first sketched out in 1859, although it had taken him over twenty years to effect his scheme.

Owen was a vigorous anti-evolutionist and his floor plan was intended to assist illustration of Divine Purpose in the creation of the species. In that respect the Museum has greatly changed: it contains a gallery devoted to Darwin and the theory of evolution and another with a particularly clear account of the ancestors of *Homo sapiens*. Many of the displays of groups of animals and plants, as well as spectacular presentations of the history of the Earth and the development of the British landscape, are offered in an evolutionary context. The Museum is a major international research centre and in that respect its internal managerial organization is much as Owen left it: its research departments now are zoology, botany, entomology, palaeontology, and mineralogy. But the public displays, which changed relatively little in the Museum's first century, have been vividly modernized in the past two decades.

Most of the public displays are organized as 'themes'; apart from those mentioned, there are also to be found galleries devoted respectively to ecology, dinosaurs, human biology, gemstones, the oil and gas deposits of the North Sea, arthropods (called 'creepy crawlies' by the Museum's popularizers), geological evidence of the passage of time, mammals, fishes and reptiles, marine invertebrates, meteorites, birds, the geology of the British Isles, British natural history, British fossils, rocks and minerals from around the world, and building materials.

Despite the brilliance of the displays, the science is relatively superficial in the first few items of this list. In some of the later items traces

Diamond crystals: clockwise from top right, in beach conglomerate from Namaqualand, in kimberlite from South Africa and in matrix from Siberia.

remain of the former display policy of the Museum, by which the visitor was left to find some personal way of dealing with rows of cases of only slightly differing materials. However, the museum authorities are steadily working through the galleries to bring them all into the twenty-first century.

The Diplodocus skeleton in the Central Hall remains as impressive as it has been for the past century, but the aerial walkway through Gallery 21 now places the visitors above the other dinosaurs and diminishes accordingly their former immensity. Nothing, however, can reduce the overwhelming power of the blue whale in Gallery 24, beside which the Indian elephants seem the size of large dogs and the pygmy elephants mere puppies.

It is well worth climbing the staircase in the Central Hall. Firstly, one can then appreciate the magnitude of the building and its architectural splendour. Secondly, doing so provides access to the exhibition of Man's Place in Evolution in Gallery 101 and the particularly attractive display of British Natural History in Gallery 202.

Earth sciences are dealt with for the most part within the building of the former Geological Museum, which had been erected in the 1920s to replace a still earlier museum in a building in Jermyn Street. Gallery 73 tells the Story of the Earth, with much sound of crashing tectonic plates. Busts of some of the nineteenth-century British geologists who helped classify the rocks and order them in time seem to be on their way out, but are still to be found at the back of Gallery 154, behind the collection of British minerals. The marble busts stare at Gallery 153 which demonstrates the geology of Britain's Offshore Oil and Gas, the present source of power and wealth. But much wealth still remains in Gemstones, luxuriantly displayed in Gallery 72. And not to be missed is the moving account of Earthquakes in Gallery 74, where the floor shakes beneath the visitors' feet while a screen shows pictures of an earthquake in California. Apart from the public displays, the Museum is an immense repository of reference information; this is not normally accessible to visitors, but can be seen by prior arrangement with the Curators or Librarians. Within the Museum are five very large libraries (see p.131). The Herbarium is one of the most important in the world, with an exceptional collection of original type specimens. And there are vast collections of those objects that natural historians have been gathering for several centuries — butterflies, birds' eggs, bones, etc.

A modern model of an ancient Chinese apparatus, dated 132 AD and invented by Zhang Heng, for detecting earthquakes.

North Woolwich
Old Station Museum

Pier Road, North Woolwich E16 2JJ
Tel: 071-474 7244

Rail: North Woolwich
Bus: 69, 101, 276
Limited car parking in adjacent streets

Opening times: Mon-Wed and Sat 10.00-17.00, Sun and Bank Holidays 14.00-17.00
Admission: free

Library
Access for wheelchairs
Group visits: write to or telephone the museum office

The museum, on the bank of the Thames, occupies what was a spacious railway station until 1979. The station, which was originally erected (in 1854) by the Great Eastern Railway, once served the G.E.R.'s own ferry, the charge for which was one penny, as well as the rail service. But the former was put out of business in 1889 by the introduction of the civic free ferry, still sailing, and the latter now runs alongside to a tiny and less costly terminus. So the main hall, the ticket office, the ladies' waiting room and the guards' and drivers' sitting room in the imposing old building have been filled with railway memorabilia and model trains. Behind the station are items of signalling equipment and a portable ticket office, and on the formerly-active railway line sit elderly locomotives (one dating from 1876) and carriages.

An 0-6-0 saddle-tank engine, built by Robert Stephenson & Hawthorn Ltd in 1952, on the line behind the Museum.

Old Operating Theatre, Museum & Herb Garret

9a St Thomas's Street, Southwark SE1 9BY
Tel: 071-955 4791

Underground: London Bridge
Rail: London Bridge
Bus: 17, 21, 22a, 35, 40, 43, X43, 47, 48, 133, 214, 344, 501,505, 521,
D1, D11, P3, P11

Opening times: Tues-Sun 10.00-16.00
Admission: ££ (concessions)

Group visits: write to or telephone the museum beforehand

This remarkable museum is one of the most gruesome in London. St Thomas's Hospital was, from the twelfth century, an annexe of the church in which the museum is housed, although the hospital expanded steadily on the adjacent land until it moved to its present site in Lambeth, opposite the Houses of Parliament, in 1862. In the early nineteenth century, the need for more surgical facilities in the hospital led to the construction of an operating theatre for women patients within the roof of the church.

This arrangement allowed direct access for the patients from a third-floor women's ward, with separate access for the students and other spectators who arrived by climbing the stairs of the church tower, which present-day visitors must also use. Part of the space within the church roof had been used as a 'herb garret' — i.e. the apothecaries' store room — from very early days in the history of the hospital.

In the small museum area, a corner is given over to the herbs prescribed by the physicians, and to the pestles and mortars used for grinding them. In the remainder of the space there are now displayed a few items of a general domestic kind — pots, pans and mugs — and a large collection of surgical implements, grouped by periods, from early medieval times to the late nineteenth century.

Alongside these, the written accounts on the walls document the progress of hospital treatment through the ages and are supplemented by copies of various

The tower of the former St Thomas's Church which houses the Old Operating Theatre.

The old operating theatre.

contemporary illustrations of surgical practice in the days before either anaesthesia or aseptic conditions. One therefore enters the old operating theatre very conscious of the scenes that would have been enacted there: desperate screaming patients held down by three or four assistants while the frock-coated surgeon was sawing or chiselling away.

And in the theatre, there it all is: the crude wooden operating table, the box of saw-dust on the floor to catch the blood, the basin in which the surgeon may have washed his hands at the end of the session, though only very rarely before it, and the peg on which he hung his outdoor coat when he donned the working coat, stained and stinking with blood and pus. And round the working area rise the tiers of seats that accommodated, at the lower level, the visitors who came for the entertainment and, at the higher levels, the students who hoped to learn good surgical practice by demonstration.

A tour of this museum takes between half an hour and an hour and it is recommended to all those with strong stomachs; but also to any who doubt if our quality of life has significantly improved over the years. The inscription on the wall of the theatre, '*Miseratione non Mercede*' ('For compassion, not for gain'), was no doubt sincerely meant, but the expression of it brought terror and fierce pain to its subjects, and about half of them died of the after-effects.

Old Royal Observatory

Greenwich, SE10 9NF
Tel: 081-858 4422

Rail: Greenwich, Maze Hill; Docklands Light Railway to Island Gardens
Bus: 53, 53X, 177, 180, 286
Free car parking in Greenwich Park

Opening times: April-September: Mon-Sat 10.00-18.00, Sun 12.00-18.00 October-March:
Mon-Sat 10.00-17.00, Sun 14.00-17.00
Admission: £££ (concessions and 'passport' ticket)

Group visits: write to or telephone the Education Department (081-312 6608)
or the Visitors Services Manager (081 312 6603)
Library and Maritime Information Centre in National MaritimeMuseum

This group of buildings, in their dramatic setting on the site of a fifteenth-century fortress high above the Thames, constitutes a scientific centre not to be missed by those seeking the links between London and science. Charles II decreed the establishment of a Royal Observatory in 1675. Its first building, of which the architect was Christopher Wren, himself a former professor of astronomy at Gresham College, is now called Flamsteed House.

Flamsteed was the first Astronomer Royal and served from 1675 until his death in 1719. The Royal Observatory was moved to Herstmonceux Castle in Sussex in the early 1950s. In the 275 years of the Observatory's presence at Greenwich, the Astronomers Royal included such great names as Halley, Bradley, Maskelyne, Airy and Adams; and new buildings were erected from time to time.

When he founded the observatory, King Charles II required his astronomer 'to apply himself with the most exact care and diligence to the rectifying the tables of the motions of the heavens, and the places of the fixed stars, so as to find out the so-much-desired longitude of places for the perfecting the art of navigation.' Accurate

Harrison's marine chronometer, H1.

A marker carrying the Prime Meridian of the World.

The Greenwich Time Ball.

determinations of stellar co-ordinates, in turn depending on accurate time-keeping, have been among the leading activities of the work of the staff of the Observatory, in obedience to the instruction of King Charles. This was because, until the recent developments of electronic methods, coupled now with signals beamed from earth satellites, the only way of determining the longitude of a ship out of sight of land was by comparison at an exactly known time of observed stellar co-ordinates with reliable tabulated values. The accuracy of the work of the Observatory led in 1884 to the international adoption, as the Prime Meridian of the World, of a meridian calculated by the Greenwich astronomers. This is the line of zero longitude, and the line from which daily time (Greenwich Mean Time) is reckoned.

In the courtyard adjacent to the Meridian Building and Flamsteed House, the meridian is marked by a laser strip aligned with Airy's Transit Circle. For most hours of summer days when the weather is dry, it is bestridden by visitors being photographed with one foot in the eastern hemisphere and one in the western.

Within Flamsteed House are displayed some old astronomical instruments — astrolabes, celestial globes, qiblas (used to determine the direction of Mecca from the position of the stars) and early telescopes — together with a reconstruction of Flamsteed's living quarters and the beautifully restored Octagon Room, designed by Wren as Flamsteed's observing chamber. Other buildings contain collections of time-keeping instruments, including Harrison's clock which gained him the Admiralty prize of £20,000 for a chronometer that would keep accurate time at sea. And the Telescope Dome contains the 28 inch telescope of 1893, the largest refractor in the country.

The South Building, formerly a physics laboratory and subsidiary observatory, has been converted into a planetarium. However, the presentations in the planetarium are somewhat irregular and the visitor wishing to attend is advised to enquire about times beforehand.

One other world-renowned feature of the Observatory is the Time Ball. This large red sphere, mounted on a shaft on one of the small towers that surmount Flamsteed House, is dropped daily at precisely 13.00 hours. Originally this was done to allow the chronometers of vessels sailing on the Thames to be set accurately; now the custom is maintained for historical colour.

The Museum seen from beneath the wings of mounted Supermarine Spitfire IX and Hawker Hurricane fighter planes.

Royal Air Force Museum

Grahame Park Way, NW9 5LL
Tel: 081-205 2266; 081-205 9191 (information)

Underground: Colindale (then bus)
Rail: Mill Hill Broadway (then bus)
Bus: 32, 113, 221, 226, 292, 303
By road: via A41, A5, A1(M), M1(J4), M11, M25, or North Circular (A406)
Car park (free)

Opening times: Daily 10.00-18.00
Admission: £££ (concessions)

Restaurant
Access for wheelchairs
Group visits: contact the General Services Manager (081-205 2266)

This is Britain's national museum of aviation and contains an international variety of aeroplanes, although the great majority are those that have seen service in the Royal Air Force. Nearly all exhibits are merely on display: visitors cannot enter them. Exceptions are a Jet Provost fuselage and cockpit which offers a 'touch and try' experience, with working controls, and a Tornado Flight Simulator, both much appreciated by visitors of all ages.

The exhibits offer vivid evidence of the rapid development of flight technology through the twentieth century. They begin with observers' balloons which travelled only as fast as the wind would carry them; they end with machines that fly at several times the speed of sound. A view into the cockpit of a Phantom illustrates the complexity of modern military flight.

An Avro Lancaster bomber which took part in 137 operations from East Anglia to enemy territory in Europe during the 1939-1945 War.

A brief lecture-demonstration lasting about 20 minutes and given from time to time through the day provides an exceptionally clear account of the aerodynamic principles involved in the powered flight of heavier-than-air machines. Other technical displays deal, by means of models and video presentations, with jet propulsion, height and speed recording, radio and radar. Also, interesting historical films are regularly presented in the museum's cinema.

The various aircraft exhibitions, a display about London in the blitz of 1940-1941, and the restaurant are all housed in former hangars so that the ambience has the feel of an aerodrome, which indeed the site once was. But although the hangars then contained aeroplanes, the corridors were not at the time decorated with the two fine sculptures now on show: *Icarus* by Michael Ayrton and *Winged Figure* by Elizabeth Frink.

Royal Armouries, Tower of London

The Royal Armouries, HM Tower of London, EC3N 4AB
Tel: 071-480 6358

Underground: Tower Hill, Tower Gateway
Rail: London Bridge, Fenchurch Street
Bus: 15, 42, 78, 100, D1, D9, D11
Adjacent car park

Opening times: Mar-Oct: Mon-Sat, Bank Holidays 9.30-18.00; Sun 14.00-18.00
Nov-Apr: Mon-Sat, Bank Holidays 9.30-16.00; Sun 10.00-17.45
Admission: £££ (concessions)

Restaurant
Access for wheelchairs
Group visits: write to or telephone the Visitors Service Department (071-488 5694)

The Tower of London is a major repository, museum and centre for romance, legend, history and architecture. Here we are concerned only with the Royal Armouries, an unrivalled collection of the hardware of mainly European military science with exhibits up to 1,200 years old, though mostly from the sixteenth to the nineteenth centuries. The major part of the collection fills the White Tower, the 900-year-old central building of the Tower complex, but spills over into the New Armouries on the eastern side of the Tower site.

On view are arms and armour from the eighth century onwards. Neither the beautiful decorations with which some weapons are enriched, nor the elegant geometry of many of the displays, manage to hide the deathly quality of the exhibits. Even the ceremonial weapons look alarmingly lethal; and the technical skill that went into the design and manufacture of the weapons of combat is awesome. On display indoors are small arms, from early matchlocks and flintlocks to relatively modern rifles, with muskets, carbines, blunderbusses and even a steam-driven machine gun shown on the way, and within the display galleries and on the roads outside are cannon, mortars and bombards.

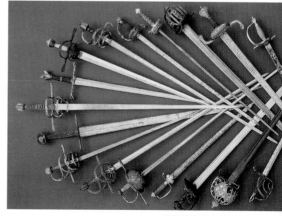

A decorative arrangement of swords from the fifteenth to the nineteenth centuries.

Royal Botanic Gardens, Kew

Kew Green, Richmond, Surrey TW9 3AB
Tel: 081-940 1171

Underground: Kew Gardens
Rail: Kew Gardens, Kew Bridge
Bus: 65, 391
Limited street car parking

Opening times: in winter daily 9.30-16.00; in summer Mon-Sat 9.30-18.30,
Sun and Public Holidays 9.30-20.00
Admission: £££ (concessions)

Restaurants
Access for wheelchairs
Photography: allowed but permission required for use of tripods
Group visits: contact the Enquiry Unit (081-332 5622)

Decimus Burton's Palm House, with the Water Lily House in the background.

The Royal Botanic Gardens, Kew, is claimed in its guide book to be 'in effect an encyclopaedia of living and preserved plants, a garden and a green laboratory.' It is, indeed, all of these and something else besides: a unique experience of the richness of plant life from the four corners of the world, of unrivalled beauty when the weather permits, of riveting interest whatever the weather.

The gardens today cover about 300 acres (120 ha) of land lying on the Surrey (southern) bank of the River Thames just above Kew Bridge. They have their origin in the 9 acres (3.5 ha) of her estate formalized as a botanical garden in 1769 by Princess Augusta, daughter-in-law of George II and mother of George III. This was in the area of the Broad Walk, south of the Orangery.

After Augusta's death (1772), George III combined his own Richmond estate, which occupied the western part of the gardens, running alongside the river, with that which had been his mother's and this combination forms most of the present gardens. The formal gardens were then greatly extended under the enthusiastic direction of Sir Joseph Banks, President of the Royal Society; the less formal part of the estate was landscaped and tended with no less care by the royal gardeners.

At this period the whole estate, although of world renown as a result of Banks's commissioning of plant-collection on an intercontinental basis, remained private royal property. However, in 1840 parts of the grounds were handed over to the state and the botanic gardens, under the direction of Sir William Hooker, were soon after opened to the public. Further donations of land and buildings by the crown during the next sixty-five years raised the area of the gardens to the present size.

The history of the Royal Botanic Gardens has ensured that, for more than two and a quarter centuries, gardeners and botanists have set and cultivated trees and other plants with every care and attention. In addition, high-quality architects have designed buildings, landscapes and vistas which delight the eye from every angle as well as providing, in the stately glasshouses and conservatories, a

The Kew Pagoda.

range of environments in which all manner of vegetable forms can be grown in the most appropriate conditions.

The result is magnificent living history. You can sit in the shade of mature exotic trees, brought to Kew from Australasia or the Americas in the eighteenth century; you can marvel at waterlilies first introduced during the reign of Queen Victoria; or you can walk through a conservation area (around Queen Charlotte's Cottage) which has remained unchanged for 100 years.

Equally, you can appreciate the architectural glories of the eighteenth-century pagoda, or the nineteenth-century Palm House, or the twentieth-century Princess of Wales Conservatory. Another delight is to look at flowers through the eyes of painters — either pictures in the rich permanent collection of paintings in the Marianne North Gallery, or those in the temporary exhibitions mounted in the Kew Gardens Gallery.

Right: The Rhododendron Dell at Kew.

Below: A view of the interior of the Temperate House.

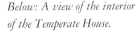

The gardens now boast a collection of nearly 40,000 plant species, so it is physically impossible to examine all that is on view in one day's visit. And although there are many limited areas devoted to special groups of plants — the woodland garden, the rock garden, the alpine garden, the grass garden (a special marvel), and a host of others — the disposition of the plants is for the most part not systematic in a botanical sense. The one exception is the group of Order Beds in the Herbaceous Ground area in the north-east corner. These were set out by Sir Joseph Hooker, son of Sir William whom he succeeded as Director in 1865. The herbaceous plants in the Order Beds, including plants of medicinal or edible interest, are associated by family to assist students of botany and horticulture in distinguishing the different species.

The Royal Botanic Gardens have been instrumental in effecting economic developments of cultivation which have significantly changed world trading patterns. One of the most important of these came about by the germination of seeds of the South American rubber tree, *Hevea brasiliensis*, brought to Kew in 1876 by Henry Wickham; the seedlings were rapidly shipped to Ceylon (Sri Lanka) and their descendants formed the vast plantations of Malaya and Indonesia, which supply the bulk of the world's natural rubber. Mature rubber trees derived from the same stock can be seen in Decimus Burton's imposing Palm House. This house also contains specimens of the bread-fruit tree, *Artocarpus altilis*, carried in 1792 from Tahiti to the West Indies by Captain Bligh (see p.207), whence a few specimens were brought on to Kew.

To emphasize the consequences of the work at Kew, Sir William Hooker established in 1847 a Museum of Economic Botany. The old buildings have recently been closed and replaced by the elegant Sir Joseph Banks Building in the northernmost corner of the gardens. This exciting structure, beautifully situated on and reflected by a small lake, houses the Economic Botany collection, although this is not accessible to visitors. What visitors do get is a very modern-style presentation about the origin and uses of cellulose, with multiple screens, video monitors, circumambient sound, and pop-up figures of peasants of varied origin — far livelier than Hooker's museum, but providing only a fraction of the information that was formerly offered.

A visit to Kew is highly recommended, but those intending to make one should plan knowingly. Firstly, it is necessary to be aware that there is much walking to be done, so suitable clothing is very important: appropriate shoes, and general covering to match the weather. If this can be arranged, there is no reason to avoid either very hot days or very wet ones. Secondly, plenty of time should be scheduled — all day, if possible. Thirdly, heavy impedimenta — camera tripods (which in any case require special permission to be used within the glasshouses), easels and paints or drawing equipment (same restriction), big binoculars, etc. — should normally be left at home, since their weight seems to increase steadily through the day. Fourthly, although picnic areas are provided, and indeed you can picnic in non-designated areas, to set out intending to have a picnic implies carrying baskets of food on the long walks; the more comfortable alternative is to use one of several restaurants and cafeterias to be found within the gardens.

Wild Flowers of Chanleon-Chili,
painting by Marianne North (1830-1890).

Royal College of General Practitioners Museum

14 Princes Gate, Hyde Park, SW7 1PU
Tel: 071-581 3232

Underground: Knightsbridge, South Kensington, Kensington High Street
Rail: Victoria
Bus: 9, 10, 14, 52

Opening times: 10.00-16.00
Admission: only to professionally interested visitors, arranged by prior appointment with
the Curator or Librarian

Library: admission only by prior appointment and at the discretion of the Librarian
Photography: not allowed

The Museum holds a modest collection of about 800 items donated by practitioners since the College was established in 1952. In contrast to surgeons, physicians rarely collect pathological specimens and the tools of their trade do not generally include the aggressive implements of the operating theatre, although country doctors sometimes carried a small saw for emergency amputations, as shown in the contents of a nineteenth-century medical bag.

So the objects on display here are medicine chests of the kind that GPs once kept in their surgeries, old-fashioned clinical thermometers, sphygmomanometers, aspirators, and cupping sets. Together with some nineteenth-century microscopes is a splendid Culpeper microscope of the eighteenth century. Among other interesting old instruments is a Dudgeon sphygmograph and the old stethoscopes include several wooden ones of the Laennec type. There is also a collection of materia medica as was used by the Royal Army Medical Corps.

The Royal College of General Practitioners.

Royal College of Obstetricians and Gynaecologists Museum

27 Sussex Place, NW1 4RG
Tel: 071-262 5425

Underground: Baker Street
Rail: Marylebone
Bus: 13, 82, 113, 139, 274
Car parking (free in Regent's Park)

Opening times: Mon-Fri 10.00-17.00
Admission: only to Fellows, Members and professionally interested visitors, arranged by
prior appointment with the Curator or Librarian

Library: admission only by prior appointment and only to research workers
or professionally involved people at the discretion of the Librarian

Group visits: contact the Librarian

Obstetrics and gynaecology were Cinderella subjects until well into the present
century. Midwives — not all as frightening as Dickens' Mrs Gamp — were
regarded by the medical and surgical establishments as the only proper people
to attend women in labour, even though 'gentlemen-midwives' had been in active practice
since early in the seventeenth century. Not until 1929 did the obstetricians and gynaecol-
ogists succeed in establishing their own College, given the title 'Royal' in 1938. It moved in 1960 into its present elegant and spacious premises.

On display in the museum is a unique set of seventeenth-century instruments — the Chamberlen collection of forceps, levers, crotchets, etc. — showing that the essentials of modern solutions to obstetric problems were appreciated 300 years ago. Most obstetric instruments from the succeeding three centuries display gradual refinements of design. New instruments appear over the years — dilators, perforators, cranioclasts, cephalotribes, and others — mostly to be abandoned but some to be improved by the experience of generations of obstetricians.

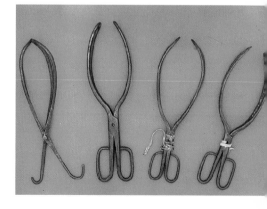

Seventeenth-century obstetric forceps from the Chamberlen collection.

Interior of the Hunterian Museum.

Royal College of Surgeons of England Museums

Hunterian Museum; Odontological Museum; Wellcome Museum of Anatomy; Wellcome
Museum of Pathology

35-43 Lincoln's Inn Fields, WC2A 3PN
Tel: 071-405 3474

Underground: Holborn, Temple
Bus: 1, 8, 22B, 25, 68, 98, 168, 171, 188, 196, 501, 505, 521

Opening times: Mon-Fri 10.00-17.00
Admission: only to professionally interested visitors, arranged by prior appointment with
the Museums Secretary (ext.3011), preferably by letter; for visits solely to the
Wellcome Museum of Anatomy, apply to the Curator (ext. 3100)

Library: admission only by prior appointment with the Librarian (ext.3000)
Photography: not usually allowed
Group visits: by prior arrangement, by letter or telephone, with the Museums Secretary

A wartime German bomb in 1941 destroyed most of the building of the Royal College of Surgeons. About twenty per cent of the 65,000 specimens in the College's great museum collections were recovered from the rubble behind the façade, which happened to remain more or less intact.

Over the next twenty-five years the collections were re-examined and re-arranged: some specimens went to the Natural History Museum and elsewhere, and others were augmented with new material. The present group of museums was reconstructed out of the earlier collections. They now offer a unique study and reference facility for students and practitioners of medicine, dentistry, veterinary science and nursing, as well as medical historians and students of zoology. And uniformly the four museums provide detailed explanatory annotations of the specimens which, in turn, are set out in a rational order for the most effective pedagogic value.

THE HUNTERIAN MUSEUM

The great surgeon and anatomist John Hunter (1728-1793) began his professional career as assistant in the Anatomy School of his brother William Hunter. In 1763 he established his own school, which he later associated with his private museum in Leicester Square. By the time of Hunter's death, the museum contained above 17,000 specimens. Hunter's collection formed the core of the museum of the Royal College of Surgeons, which was greatly enlarged in the nineteenth century.

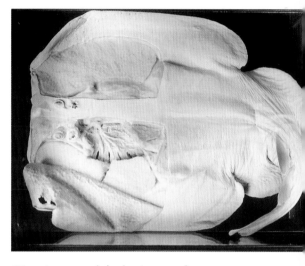

The present display, like the original, is essentially a teaching resource. Also like the original, it is for the most part organized on the basis of the comparative anatomy of physiological function: move-

Dissection to reveal the electric organ of Torpedo galvanii, *displayed in the Hunterian Museum.*

ment, respiration, digestion, nervous system, musculature, and so on. A second important series consists of pathological items arranged to explain dysfunction as well as function. A particularly valuable osteological collection, built up in the nineteenth and early twentieth centuries, was badly damaged by the wartime bombing, but a small part of it remains.

Hunter was an avidly committed collector, anxious to be able to demonstrate abnormal as well as normal material to his students. People regularly brought him odd or curious specimens. The unusual items in his own collection were added to later. As a result, there are now on display many rare pathological conditions, including the skeletons of giants and a dwarf, grafts, odd animals and the like. In addition, there are some of Hunter's instruments to be seen, and also histological slides prepared by John Quekett, the museum Conservator in the middle of the nineteenth century.

THE ODONTOLOGICAL MUSEUM

This museum displays nearly everything that has relevance to the anatomy and pathology of teeth and to the practice of dentistry. Members of the Odontological Society, founded in 1856 but merged with the Royal Society of Medicine half a century later, established an early museum which developed into this one. The original collection has been considerably enlarged and a few relevant items once in Hunter's collection have also been added to it.

On display are specimens illustrating the comparative anatomy of vertebrate jaws and teeth, a wide range of dental diseases and pathologies, extraction instruments from the eighteenth century to recent times, dentures up to 200 years old, and a case devoted to the Piltdown forgery, in which a significant part was played by the forged teeth. Sir Arthur Keith, a former conservator, was involved in early controversies surrounding the Piltdown skull.

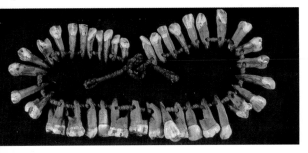

Above: A necklace of human teeth brought back from the Congo by the explorer H. M. Stanley.

Right: Interior of the Odontological Museum.

THE WELLCOME MUSEUM OF PATHOLOGY

This excellent teaching collection is restricted to human pathology. The beautifully prepared specimens cover a very wide range of pathological conditions found in the body's organs and systems. They make ideal examples for pathology examination questions and indeed the museum is often used as the venue for the conduct of such examinations. As well as diseased tissues, the museum also displays a fine array of medical instruments, including some used by Lister, and also a Laennec stethoscope. Other general instruments include specimens from the eighteenth to the twentieth centuries.

THE WELLCOME MUSEUM OF ANATOMY

This museum, restricted to human anatomy, provides another excellent teaching collection. As with the pathology museum, the specimens are beautifully preserved and displayed and often serve as the examples for examination questions.

Royal London Hospital

Medical College Museum and Hospital Archives & Museum

London Hospital Medical College, Turner Street, E1 2AD (Museum)
Royal London Hospital, Whitechapel, E1 1BB (Archives)
Tel: 071-377 7000 (Museum ext.3027; Archives ext.3364)

Underground: Whitechapel
Bus: 25, 253, 106

Opening times: 10.00-16.30
(closed Bank Holidays and for one week at Christmas and Easter)
Admission: the Medical College Museum is open only to members of the health
professions, by prior appointment with the Curator

Library: by prior arrangement with the Librarian
Access for wheelchairs to both Archives and Museum
Photography: not allowed
Group visits: contact the Curator

The London Hospital (now the Royal London Hospital) was founded in 1759 and built on comparatively open land, but in the last century and a half of its existence it has been engulfed by London's East End, the poorer side of the city. As a result, the hospital has particular experience of the diseases of poverty, as well as the conditions that affect everyone.

The London Hospital Medical School Museum was set up to aid the teaching of pathology, and now has about 4,000 specimens in the collection, arranged by system. Like the museums in the other London medical schools, it is actively used by teachers and students, so that access is not always possible in term time. The museum has a rich collection of specimens of occupational diseases, including examples of 'phossy jaw' from a nearby match factory at the turn of the century and the first open heart operation (by Sir Henry Souttar in 1925, the patient dying twelve years later).

The Royal London Hospital Archives are freely open to the public. They contain all the records and collected objects of the hospital other than the pathology specimens.

The Royal London Hospital, *1990. painting, acrylic on board, by Professor John P. Blandy, FRCS.*

. Royal Pharmaceutical Society Museum

1 Lambeth High Street, SE1 7JN
Tel: 071-735 9141

Underground: Vauxhall, Westminster, Waterloo, Lambeth North
Rail: Vauxhall, Waterloo
Bus: 3, 76, 77, 159, 510
Nearby car park (paying)

Opening times: Mon-Fri 9.00-17.00 by prior appointment with the Curator or Librarian
Admission: free

Library
Limited access for wheelchairs
Photography: not allowed without prior permission
Group visits: arranged only by prior appointment with the Curator

The Royal Pharmaceutical Society of Great Britain was founded in 1841 and had premises in Bloomsbury Square before moving to the present modern building. The Society's museum was set up in 1842 and is the only collection of its kind in the country solely devoted to pharmaceutical material. Although it was formed as a teaching and reference collection of materia medica, the museum today is a repository of all relevant historical material. It has a particularly fine collection of English pharmaceutical delftware and other ceramic objects, pharmaceutical glassware, pewter, silver, etc.

It also houses a collection of old pharmaceutical instruments for weighing, measuring and dispensing. There are several historically important collections of materia medica and a substantial collection of proprietary medicines.

The Society possesses a collection of ephemera of pharmaceutical interest, including pharmacists' records, advertising literature, and a collection of caricatures — prints and drawings illustrating the developments of pharmacy and medicine from the seventeenth to the twentieth century. The library provides reference access to historical information as well as current practices and procedures.

Various old pharmaceutical items, including a leech jar, delft jar, paper holder and scales.

St Bartholomew's Museum of Pathology

St Bartholomew's Medical College, West Smithfield EC1A 7BE
Tel: 071-601 8888

Underground: Farringdon, Barbican, St Paul's
Rail: Moorgate
Bus: 4, 8, 22B, 25, 56, 141, 153, 172, 279, 501

Opening times: by prior appointment with the Professor of Histopathology
Admission: only to professionally interested visitors, arranged by prior appointment

Library: admission only by prior appointment and at the discretion of the Librarian
Photography: allowed only by prior arrangement

The museum of the medical school of London's oldest established hospital is a heavily-used teaching facility as well as a treasury of many medical curiosities. The museum was established by Percival Pott, chief surgeon of St Bartholomew's Hospital at the end of the eighteenth century and developed by Sir James Paget, chief surgeon in the middle of the nineteenth century.

There are inevitably specimens illustrating Pott's disease of the spine and the scrotal carcinoma in chimneysweeps first described by him. There are photographs and bones from Paget's original patient with his eponymous disease of bone. But the museum also holds an extensive teaching collection of normal and pathological specimens of all organs and parts of the body. Furthermore, a plaque on the wall of a room off the museum claims it to be the location of the utterance of the words, 'I see you have lately returned from Afghanistan,' — Sherlock Holmes's introductory remark to Dr Watson on the occasion of their first meeting, when Holmes was working in a laboratory at Bart's.

The Henry VIII gate, St Bartholomew's Hospital.

St John Ambulance Museum

St John's Gate, St John's Lane, Clerkenwell EC1M 4DA
Tel: 071-253 6644

Underground: Farringdon, Barbican
Rail: Farringdon, King's Cross
Bus: 55, 243, 503, 505 (to Clerkenwell Road); 4 (to Aldersgate Street, Goswell Road);
277, 279 (to St John Street)

Opening times: Mon-Fri 10.00-17.00; Sat 10.00-16.00
Admission: free

Library: admission only by prior appointment
Access for wheelchairs
Group visits: write to or telephone the library staff or the Assistant Curator

St John's Gate, south side.

The religious Order of St John was founded in the twelfth century in Jerusalem with a particular duty to care for sick pilgrims. The English branch of the Order had its headquarters in the Priory of Clerkenwell, of which St John's Gate was then the main entrance.

When Henry VIII disestablished the monasteries in 1540 the English branch was dissolved and over the centuries most of the Priory buildings were replaced. However, a British Order of St John was revived in the early nineteenth century and managed to acquire St John's Gate as its headquarters. The St John Ambulance Brigade was formed by the British Order in 1887 to provide a corps of volunteer first aid workers who would assist the medical services in peace and war, as well as in teaching the public the principles of first aid.

The Ambulance Museum collection contains Victorian litters, first aid kits and manuals produced and used in the Brigade's 100-year history, and documents relating to the Brigade's co-operation with the British Red Cross Society. The Museum of the Order of St John, in the same building, has on display some sixteenth-century drug jars from the Order's Maltese pharmacy and an account of the work of the British Ophthalmic Hospital in Jerusalem, founded by the Order in 1882.

Science Museum

(National Museum of Science and Industry)

Exhibition Road, SW7 2DD
Tel: 071-938 8000

Underground: South Kensington
Bus: 9, 10, 14, 30, 33, 45, 49, 52, 52A, 74, 503, C1

Opening times: Mon-Sat 10.00 - 18.00; Sun 11.00 - 18.00
Admission: £££ (concessions)

Restaurants
Library
Access for wheelchairs
Photography: allowed without flash
Group visits: write to or telephone the Group Bookings Office (071-938 8191)
Educational groups: write to the Educational Booking Office

The institution that Londoners know as the Science Museum is the flagship of the National Museum of Science and Technology. It has branches in other parts of the country, but these are not considered further here. The museum has been on

The Lotus Sport pursuit bicycle on which Chris Boardman won a gold medal in the 1992 Olympics at Barcelona shown here in Science Box, the temporary display area near the Museum's entrance.

its present site in South Kensington since 1929 and has been a source of delight, fascination and instruction to visitors of all ages from the time it opened. Each year it attracts about 1.3 million visitors — only a few less than its giant neighbour, the Natural History Museum. However, that neighbour is housed in a building conceived in a different architectural spirit from the one that guided the design of the Science Museum.

While the Natural History Museum is meant to be a temple to the living world, the Science Museum building is rather a functional container for whatever treasures may accumulate within it. The result is to provide the visitor with a splendid collection and attempts to explain what it signifies, but awkwardly arranged in an ungainly, long, thin, six-storied edifice in which the architect might have been trying to entomb science, rather than to liberate it for the modern world.

Charles Babbage's first Difference Engine.

The visitor arriving here is well advised to buy a copy of the short *Guide to the Science Museum*. Apart from providing the obvious information, this gives suggestions for the best ways in which to spend a short visit and also draws attention to the most notable exhibits on each floor as well as including maps showing where these exhibits are to be found. But the visitor must also be forewarned: the range and extent of the displays on show here are of a complexity rivalled in London only by the British Museum. As a result, even if a whole day is spent there, the Science Museum cannot be properly covered.

The Director and staff of the Science Museum face another set of problems not encountered by museum staff elsewhere. The desire is to present science as it is now, but also to reveal it in its historical context. Yet science changes at a rate well beyond that with which museums can keep pace. For example, computers have not merely appeared on the scene in the past few decades, but have very substantially changed the practices of advanced societies.

This time scale is necessarily alarming to a Museum Curator who might normally expect a group of exhibits to remain valid for half a century or more.

A museum display about computation requires not only the mechanical and electrical antecedents of present-day electronic computers (see Babbage's and Turing's machines on the Second Floor), but also an account of the part computers are playing in modern medical technology, in transport, in communications, in production technology, and so on, even in architecture and the fine arts. And computer technology allows a myriad new methods of presenting information. So the arrival on the scene of computers has brought about the question of whether nearly all the displays of the Science Museum should be redesigned.

At the same time, advances elsewhere in the scientific endeavour — in molecular biology, biotechnology, nuclear physics, cosmology and data transmission, to name only the most obvious — make their own demands for display space and renewal of old material. So in the Science Museum the staff, working furthermore with an inadequate budget, are in a chase in which they can never catch up. The result is that the scientifically literate visitor may think, at some point in the museum, 'That's no longer true: the method shown went out of use at least two years ago!' Let that visitor be consoled with the realization that the museum staff know about it and they are working their way through the galleries on a programme of never-ending replacement.

So what is the visitor particularly recommended? It depends: with or without children? (Incidentally, it should be mentioned that, at most times of the year, the museum is thronged with children of all nationalities — brought there by their parents during the school holidays or in school parties during term time, but all evidently keenly enjoying the experience.)

With children, go for the Launch Pad on the First Floor. This gallery gives children (and their guardians) things to do which are fun, exciting and visually attractive all at the same time. They can also be instructive if the children can be persuaded to pause for a moment between exhibits to consider what they are doing. In the Launch Pad gallery there are patient assistants, called 'Explainers', who will

The original orrery, a machine showing the motions of the planets, made for the Earl of Orrery in about 1712 and named after him.

Above: The Apollo 10 command module which carried three astronauts around the Moon in May 1969.

Left: Launch Pad, the Museum's interactive hands-on gallery.

explain and discuss the displays with the children; and there are demonstrations given from time to time of activities of a scientific or technological kind that children might try when they return home.

Adults without children may need to pick an area of interest. No doubt all are interested in health — their own at the very least — and on the Fifth and Fourth Floors they should see the Wellcome Collection of the History of Medicine. This is a display, without rival in the world, of the methods and tools of European, Asian, Arabic, African and

South American medicine and surgery. It covers a time span from the ancient Greeks to the present day.

Working your way down from the top of the museum, a new gallery on the Third Floor deals with health matters — the latest medical research and development, modern curative medicine, and trends in health and lifestyle. The flight gallery on this floor is very popular, although there is more science and some technology as well as much history on display and explained in the galleries given over to branches of physics and to photography and cinematography. Another new display here, 'Science in the eighteenth century', presents George III's collection of scientific instruments. Galleries on the Second Floor cover industrial and research chemistry and biochemistry and give a greater weight to technology and manufacture than those on the Third Floor; they also include galleries showing various aspects of ocean transport — ships, navigation, docks and diving, as well as other industries.

Galleries on the First Floor, apart from the Launch Pad area for children, have excellent displays about food and agriculture. Other galleries on this floor show what goes on in the manufacture of iron and steel, glass, gas, and plastics; and there are yet others dealing with telecommunications and with the history of the measurement of time. The most exciting display on the Ground Floor is that explaining space travel and exploration. In contrast, most of the other galleries at this level display aspects of land travel, by road and rail, powered by steam, petrol, electricity or human muscle. Also on the Ground Floor is a gallery giving a brief overview of the enormous range of the museum's exhibits.

The Science Museum display of the pure and applied physical, chemical and engineering sciences is vast and the historical collection that supports it is probably the largest in the world. Because many of the galleries contain working models, which the visitor is invited to activate by pushing a button or turning a handle, progress through the museum is slower than the visitor might have estimated from a judgement of the floor area. Fortunately, there is a choice of cafeterias (on the First and Third Floors) where rest and refreshment can be found.

Masts and rigging of a 50-gun ship of the Royal Navy establishment of 1733.

Sir John Soane's Museum

13 Lincoln's Inn Fields, WC2 3BP
Tel: 071-405 2107

Underground: Holborn, Temple
Bus: 1, 8, 22B, 25, 68, 98, 168, 171, 188, 501, 505, 521

Opening times: Tue-Sat 10.00-17.00
Admission: free

Library: admission only by prior appointment
Photography: allowed without use of flash
Group visits: write to or telephone the Museum Office

This crowded and astonishing collection, the smallest British national museum, was bequeathed to the nation by Soane, an eminent early nineteenth-century architect. Soane was a compulsive collector, but most items of the collection are limited to architectural, antiquarian, artistic or literary interests.

There is, however, an attractive French astronomical clock of 1800, a Hogarth painting, in the series *The Rake's Progress*, of a scene in The Madhouse (Bethlem Royal Hospital, see p.15) and (in the research library) models of pile-driving and drain-laying machines. The museum is in the house Soane built for himself and contains an early example of central heating by circulating hot air.

Sir John Soane's Museum.

The Barrier illuminated in evening light.

Thames Barrier Visitors' Centre

Unity Way, Woolwich Road, SE18 5NJ
Tel: 081-854 1373

Rail: Charlton
Bus: 177, 180
Car park (free coach park)

Opening times: Mon-Fri 10.00-17.00; Sat-Sun 10.30-17.30
Admission: ££ (concessions)

Restaurant
Teachers' resource room in Thames Barrier Schools Centre
Access for wheelchairs
Group visits: write to or telephone the General Office

The Greater London Council was in existence only from 1965 to 1986; one of its first acts, which may also prove to be one of the most enduring, was to initiate the study that led to the construction of the Thames Barrier. This flood control structure is one of Europe's most remarkable engineering achievements. It spans more than half a kilometre of the river and, together with the raised embankments running 32 km downstream, could contain a flood which raised the water level by more than 7 m above the datum.

The books and brochures available in the Visitors' Centre will tell you how many tens of thousands of tons of steel and concrete went into the construction; but no description in words can capture the towering immensity of the piers. Presentations and displays in the Visitors' Centre clearly explain the construction and the mechanism, but visitors should not miss going along the riverside walk to get as close as possible to the Barrier itself. Better still is to arrive by boat from Greenwich, which allows you to look at the Barrier from water level.

Tower Bridge
(Exhibition and Old Engine Rooms)

Tower Bridge, SE1 2UP
Tel: 071-378 1928

Underground: Tower Hill, London Bridge
Rail: London Bridge, Tower Gateway (Dockland Light Railway)
Bus: 15, 78 (to Tower Hill); 42, 100, P11, D1 (to Tooley Street)
Adjacent car and coach park (street parking at weekends)

Opening times: daily, summer 10.00 - 17.15, winter 10.00 - 16.00
Admission: ££ (concessions)

Access for wheelchairs
Group visits: write to or telephone the Bridge

The structure which, together with Big Ben, is the international symbol of London (like the Eiffel Tower in relation to Paris, or the Statue of Liberty to New York) was built against an opposition of scorn and scepticism. The museum exhibition is presented as a series of dramatic automated displays. These outline the arguments circulating in the second half of the nineteenth century for and against the concept of the bridge.

Modern technology is able to provide lively animated images of the political arguments surrounding the building of the bridge and of the engineering problems and solutions used in its design and construction. There are, in addition, fine views of London from the walkways between the towers.

The bascules of the bridge are now raised and lowered by electric power, but the old engines which, until 1974, provided hydraulic power for the purpose are on view in the Engine Rooms. A number of mechanical models exhibit the engineering principles used in the operation of the bridge. The display in this section is followed by a splendid mock-theatrical 'opening ceremony' of the bridge as seen at the original opening in 1894.

Tower Bridge, from the east.

Skeletons of an okapi and an impala, with a quagga skeleton in the background, displayed in the Museum of Zoology and Comparative Anatomy.

University College London Museums

Geology Collections; Museum of Zoology and Comparative Anatomy; Petrie Museum of Egyptian Archaeology
(Each museum has its own Curator and opening arrangements; the Petrie Museum is open daily to all visitors, but all the museums are private and members of the public are admitted to the others only by prior appointment with the Curator.)

University College London, Gower Street, WC1E 6BT
Tel: 071-387 7050

Underground: Goodge Street, Warren Street, Euston Square
Rail: Euston, St Pancras, King's Cross
Bus: 10, 14, 18, 24, 27, 29, 30, 68, 73, 74, 134, 135, 168, 253

Opening times: Weekdays only as noted for each museum below, but all are closed on Bank Holidays, for a week at Christmas and Easter, and for up to four weeks during the summer

Students' refectories can be used by visitors
Library: admission only by prior arrangement with the Librarian
Group visits: write to or telephone the Curator of the museum in question

University College is the oldest constituent college of the University of London. The museums established within the College are teaching collections which have been assembled by departmental staff since the College's foundation in 1828. The purpose of the collections is in each case to give students the opportunity of directly examining material and objects appropriate to their studies. Except for the Petrie Museum, the collections are therefore not open to the public at times when they are being used for teaching purposes.

Fossilized ammonites in the Geology Collections.

GEOLOGY COLLECTIONS
Tel: 071-387 7050, ext.2426 (Curator)
Opening times: by appointment with the Curator

A representative selection of the objects in these collections, together with some of the most spectacular specimens, are in display cabinets in the Rock Room of the College's Department of Geological Sciences. However, the vast bulk are in cupboards and drawers in the Department's teaching laboratories and storerooms.

Successive professors and other members of staff have been scouring the surface of the earth for a century and a half to fill these cupboards and drawers. Apart from the rare vulcanological books that he left to the College library, Professor M. Johnston-Lavis bequeathed a large collection of minerals and rocks which form part of the 12,000 specimens in the stratigraphic and palaeontological collection, 8,000 specimens in the mineral collection and 12,000 specimens in the rock collection. The museum holdings are strictly study collections. Moreover, the studious scholar would need to know clearly what he or she was looking for, since there are few explanatory notes to be found.

MUSEUM OF ZOOLOGY AND COMPARATIVE ANATOMY
Tel: 071-387 7050, ext.3564 (Curator)
Opening times: Mon-Fri 10.30-17.00

This is a thoroughly old-fashioned zoological museum and all the more attractive for being so. It was started by Robert Grant, the first Professor of Zoology and Comparative Anatomy in England, and still contains some of his original specimens. Succeeding occupants of the chair have added other specimens, such as the original king crab studied by Ray Lankester. Also, the bulk of the collection left by T. H. Huxley and formerly kept at Imperial College has recently been added to the museum's holdings. These fill the display cabinets and sometimes flow out on to the tables and benches of the small hall in which they are housed.

The collections include skeletons of a large variety of bony animals, from fish, through snakes and other reptiles, to mammals, including a good collection of primate skeletons. On the way, there is the skeleton of a quagga, an extinct kind of zebra, and one of only five known in the world. In addition there is a large collection of invertebrates, pickled, fossilized, or (in the case of calcareous ones) skeletonized.

An early taxidermied specimen, possibly dating to the eighteenth century, of a two-toed sloth, in the Museum of Zoology and Comparative Anatomy.

THE PETRIE MUSEUM OF EGYPTIAN ARCHAEOLOGY
Tel: 071-387 7050, ext.2887 (Museum Enquiries)
Opening times: Mon-Fri 10.00-12.00 and 13.15-17.00
Admission: free, but donations welcome
Photography: allowed, but a charge is made

The museum holds about 80,000 antiquities, mainly from ancient Egypt, but a few coming from neighbouring countries. The collection derives from items brought back from the excavations of Sir William Flinders Petrie and his successors from the College's Department of Egyptology, from 1880 to the present day. The displays, which provide an unrivalled teaching collection, give an intimate picture of the daily life and commerce of ancient Egypt, from palaeolithic to Roman times.

Most items are domestic or personal, but there are also many weights and measures and tools of various kinds relating to the technologies of building, weaving, agriculture and other industries. A glass Roman still is the oldest example known of such an object.

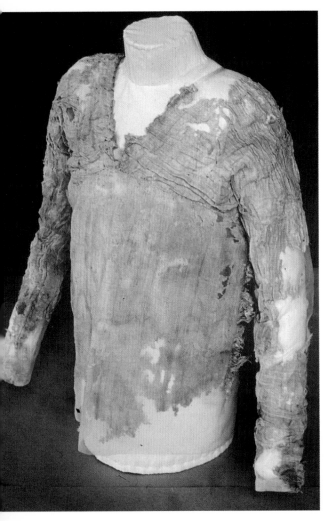

Ancient Egyptian weaving technology: a teenager's dress from Tarkhan from the time of the First Dynasty (circa 2800 BC) in the Petrie Museum. University College.

Veterinary Museum

The Royal Veterinary College, Royal College Street, NW1 0TU
Tel: 071-387 2898, ext.331

Underground: Mornington Crescent, Camden Town
Rail: Euston, King's Cross, St Pancras
Bus: 46 (to door); 24, 27, 29, 68, 134, 135, 168, 214, 253 (to Camden High Street)
Street car parking (paying)

Opening times: Mon-Fri 9.00-16.50
Admission: free (donations appreciated) arranged by prior appointment with the Archivist

Students' refectory open until 14.00
Library: admission only by prior arrangement with the Librarian
Photography: allowed if prior permission is obtained
Group visits: write to or telephone the Archivist

The museum was recently established, at the time of the College's bicentenary in 1991, and presents only a limited collection of antique implements used by veterinary surgeons. These, however, include formidable clysters, rams for obliging horses to swallow pills, fleams, and gags, as well as modest scalpels, syringes, and needles of the earlier part of the present century which could as well have been used in an operating theatre for people as well as animals. Some memorabilia of old veterinary practices are on display.

The museum also holds an important archive of books, documents, pictures and ephemera, primarily related to animal anatomy and physiology, the veterinary profession, and the history of the College.

The Royal Veterinary College,
circa *1792.*

Vintage Wireless Museum

23 Rosendale Road, West Dulwich, SE21 8DS
Tel: 081-670 3667

Underground: Stockwell (then by bus)
Rail: West Dulwich; Tulse Hill (then by bus)
Bus: 322 to door; 2, 3
Street car parking (free)

Opening times: nearly any time, before 22.00, by prior appointment
with the Curator (Mr G. Wells)
Admission: free but donations welcome

Library
Group visits: write to or telephone the Curator

Gerald Wells has given his life and his house over to this astonishing collection of a thousand wireless sets ('radio' is a barely tolerated neologism in Rosendale Road), together with gramophones, valves, dictaphones, ancient television apparatus, and memorabilia of broadcast communication up to about 1970. There are small relatively clear areas round Mr Wells's bed and round the kitchen table, but otherwise all the floor and wall space, save for the passages through, also much of the garden and even a bit of what was once a neighbour's garden, have been filled with devices covering every aspect of radio communication as well as the repair of sets. In one of the garden sheds is a

workshop where valves can be restored or even rebuilt from scratch.

Mr Wells has an intimate acquaintance with every part of every set and every circuit. If you want to know about oscillators or cathode followers, low pass filters or decouplers or super-heterodynes, then he's your man — and it would be difficult to find a more congenial guide through those mysteries.

Recreation of a 1930 wireless shop which stood in Atlantic Road, Brixton, and eventually closed in 1975.

Wellcome Centre for Medical Science

(and the Wellcome Institute for the History of Medicine)

The Wellcome Building, 183 Euston Road, NW1 2BE
Tel: 071-611 8888

Underground: Euston, Euston Square, Warren Street
Rail: Euston, St Pancras, King's Cross
Bus: 10, 14, 18, 24, 27, 29, 30, 73, 74, 134, 135

Opening times: Mon-Fri 9.45-17.00; Sat 9.45-13.00 (Closed Bank Holidays)
Admission: free

Information Service
Access for wheelchairs
Group visits to *Science for Life* exhibition: write to or telephone the
Visitor Services Co-ordinator (071-611 8649)

The Wellcome Trust was created in 1936 under the terms of the will of Sir Henry Wellcome, joint founder of the pharmaceutical company Burroughs Wellcome & Co, now Wellcome plc. The Trust was formerly the sole owner of all shares in Wellcome plc but over recent years has sold part of that holding and reinvested the proceeds. As a result, and thanks to careful and prudent trusteeship, the Trust is now one of the largest charities in the world for the promotion of medical research.

The Trust supports work not only in basic biomedical science and clinical medicine, but also in veterinary medicine

The Wellcome Building.

and the history of medicine. The Wellcome Building houses the headquarters of the Trust and also the Wellcome Centre for Medical Science and the Wellcome Institute for the History of Medicine, both of which are funded by the Trust.

The Wellcome Centre for Medical Science

The Centre is a new initiative of the Trust and provides a mixture of public facilities. Its main focus is *Science for Life*, the exhibition most immediately accessible to visitors to the Centre. This offers an exciting presentation of some key concepts in biomedical science,

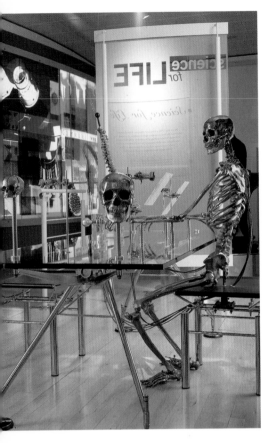

An electroplated plastic skeleton which can be manipulated by a number of levers.

using modern display technology to explain current views of physiological function, from the workings of the whole body down to those of subcellular structures. It includes a small laboratory area in which school or college groups can (by prior arrangement) be acquainted with some modern experimental research techniques.

The Information Service is in part a conventional library, specializing in science policy, the organization and management of biomedical research, research ethics, the public understanding of science, and school bioscience education. The collection of books and periodicals is combined with electronic information facilities providing data bases for searching current medical literature, a vast biomedical video collection, and an even larger collection of medical photographs. The Service collects details of many aspects of biomedical research — for example, on careers, current news, funding — and very helpful staff are always available to guide the enquirer through the maze.

On the mezzanine floor of the building there is a small permanent exhibition, *Medicine in Time*, illustrating medical themes that have remained in the forefront of human concern over millennia — plagues, arrangements for care or hospitalization, analgesics, etc. And on the top floor, in the *History of Medicine Exhibition Gallery*, temporary exhibitions are arranged on selected topics from the history of medicine. These typically feature rare and delicate materials called back from the various Wellcome collections normally on display elsewhere.

THE WELLCOME INSTITUTE FOR THE HISTORY OF MEDICINE
This Institute is a major study, teaching and research centre for the history of medicine. The Academic Unit of the Institute works in association with University College London. The library of the Institute holds half a million printed books and manuscripts on medicine and related subjects, dating from the fifteenth century to the present, and including materials of the Western and Oriental worlds.

It is the largest and most comprehensive collection in Europe of the history of medicine. The library also holds a remarkable collection of iconographic materials — paintings, drawings, prints, photographs, etc. — based on Sir Henry Wellcome's legacy, the fruit of his unparalleled collecting activity.

Wimbledon Windmill Museum

Windmill Road, Wimbledon Common, SW19 5NR
Tel: 081-947 2825

Underground: Wimbledon, Putney (then by bus)
Rail: Wimbledon, Putney (then by bus)
Bus: 93
Car park (free)

Opening times: to the public — Sat, Sun, public holidays; April-October,14.00-17.00
to school parties — weekdays, Sat a.m. during term time, by prior arrangement
Admission: £

Restaurant in adjacent building
Group visits: by prior arrangement with the honorary Curator

This fascinating mill was built in 1817 and functioned commercially until about 1870. At that date the building was converted so that eight small residences were created within the unaltered outer structure. After various modifications and partial replacement of rotted woodwork, a serious restoration programme began in the 1950s and the mill was first opened as a museum in 1976. The collection and display are still being developed, but it already probably offers a more complete account of the science and technology of windmills than any other centre in Britain.

Models show the evolutionary development of mills, up to the most modern intended for the wind generation of electric power. In addition, a collection of old devices shows the progress of winnowing and grinding corn from the use of flails, pestles and mortars, and hand querns, up to the wind- or water-powered systems, and on to the modern systems.

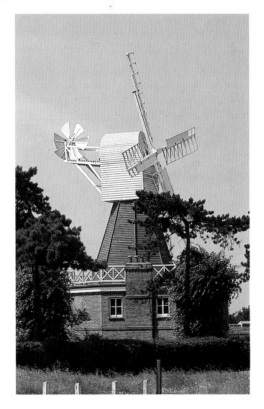

The windmill, Wimbledon Common.

CHAPTER 2

GUARDIANS OF THE SCIENCES

Teaching Centres and Learned Societies

In the centuries preceding the English Reformation, all schooling in London, as in the rest of England and the countries of Europe at that time, was controlled by the Church. Such lessons as were given were devoted almost exclusively to theology and the reading and writing of Latin. Even after the dissolution of the monasteries (1536-1540) by Henry VIII and the founding of secular grammar schools, the only augmentation of the syllabus was the addition to it of grammar and Greek.

SCHOOLS

By the middle of the nineteenth century, a view had developed that the study of Euclid was a useful mental discipline, so the grammar schools gradually began to add arithmetic and geometry to their curriculum. The sciences had been included in the curriculum of nonconformist schools from early in the eighteenth century, but there were only one or two of these in London. The grammar schools did not accept science as a valid subject of education until the very end of the nineteenth century.

By the end of the twentieth century, of course, all schools teach science subjects, although children are assured of instruction in science only until the age of sixteen. Unfortunately, the English system of secondary education obliges children to choose at that age between a science-oriented or a humanist-oriented course and significantly more of them choose the latter than the former.

Most schools, and especially the private ones, have tried to entice pupils into the sciences by installing modern teaching laboratories and successive governments have urged young people to study science. But many children apparently perceive science as difficult and offering low prospects of employment and low social esteem. It's hardly surprising, in view of this, that they turn to the arts subjects.

Left: The Senate House of the University of London in Malet Street.

Right: Pupils in a physics laboratory class at University College School, Hampstead.

Darwin wrote of the grammar school he attended in Shrewsbury that 'nothing could have been worse for the development of my mind than Dr Butler's school, as it was strictly classical, nothing else being taught except a little ancient geography and history. The school as a means of education to me was simply a blank.' Nevertheless, he succeeded as one of the world's most important scientists of the nineteenth century.

Similarly, before educational reform caught up with them, the great formal schools of London succeeded in a few cases in producing eminent scientists, despite the classicism of their syllabus. Hooke and Wren were both at Westminster School, Halley at St Paul's, Banks at Harrow before transferring to Eton, and Perkin at City of London School.

But small private schools, typically run by a single teacher, by whose name the school was known, often had a broader syllabus, to the benefit of the twenty to fifty enrolled pupils. Cavendish went to such a school in Hackney, Lister to one in Tottenham and Huxley to one in Ealing (the districts, now all well within London, being country villages at the time).

UNIVERSITIES

The University of London was founded in 1828 and professorships in the sciences were established from its start. Until that year the future scientist, whether he came from London or elsewhere in the country, wishing to study science at a university, would have been obliged to go to Oxford or Cambridge, or to one of the many Scottish universities, or else overseas.

The details of the founding and early years of the University of London are of interest only to connoisseurs of academic argumentation and rivalry. It is worth saying, though, that — despite the growth in size of the University (now by far the largest in the United Kingdom) and despite its prestige — academic rivalry persists and gives rise to a substantial re-organization of the University structure every ten to fifteen years. Suffice it to say that the University now comprises seven major colleges — University, King's, Imperial, Queen Mary, Royal Holloway, Birkbeck, and the London School of Economics, eight medical schools, several smaller colleges, and many special institutes for research and post-graduate studies.

In all, the University teaches approximately 41,000 undergraduate and 24,000 graduate students, all of whom are enrolled for full-time studies, and another 7,000 students who are enrolled for part-time studies. About 55 per cent of the undergraduates and about 30 per cent of the graduate students are pursuing studies in the sciences, engineering or medicine.

The University of London Observatory, Mill Hill.

At about the time that the University of London was being established, educational reformers were experimenting with other organizations. Foremost among such centres at the beginning of the nineteenth century were the Mechanics' Institutes, although these had been preceded at the end of the eighteenth century by the establishment of various colleges, institutes and societies concerned with science and technology. The Mechanics' Institutes aimed to give elementary instruction in mathematics and engineering to poorly educated artisans. Similar intentions led to the foundation of many other teaching centres throughout the country.

The end of the nineteenth century saw the establishment of many polytechnics. These

Two research students in the Department of Physics and Astronomy at University College London discuss a problem with their supervisor.

followed the pattern of the first, the Polytechnic in Regent Street, central London. This was founded as the Royal Polytechnic Institute in 1838 — nearly a half century after the model had been created in Paris — then re-organized and refounded in 1881 by Quintin Hogg (whose grandson, Lord Hailsham, was Britain's first Minister of Science). A character in George Bernard Shaw's play, *Man and Superman* (1903), says '... Very nice sort of place, Oxford ... They teach you to be a gentleman there. In the Polytechnic they teach you to be an engineer.'

The various polytechnic centres of higher scientific or technological education in London were initially able to award only diplomas, not recognized degrees. Over the decades of the twentieth century they evolved along a number of different paths. Some faded away; a few became colleges of the University of London; in the 1960s two (Acton and Northampton Polytechnics) became Brunel and City Universities, respectively, and a third (Battersea Polytechnic) moved away to become the University of Surrey; others, remaining as polytechnics, greatly broadened the range of subjects taught, developed faculties in the humanities, and were eventually allowed to award degrees, but only under centralized national control.

In the 1990s, however, the polytechnics have been raised by the government to independent university status. As a result, London now has twelve universities. Brunel and Kingston are within the area of Greater London although outside the London postal and telephone districts; the remainder — City, East London, Greenwich, Guildhall, Middlesex, North London, South Bank, Thames Valley and Westminster, and the University of London — are scattered over the whole metropolitan area.

Together, the universities within London now deal with about 180,000 students. Of these, about 25 per cent are part-time and about 15 per cent are graduate students, studying for master or doctoral degrees. Approximately 35 per cent of the total number are

pursuing studies in the sciences, engineering, medicine or technology, including computing and information technology. It is difficult to tell whether the proportion studying science is rising or falling as the new century approaches. Despite government attempts to increase the numbers engaged in scientific studies, there is an evident reluctance on the part of school pupils to specialize on the science side.

The universities, with financial encouragement from the government, offer various temptations to attract applicants into the science faculties: easier admission conditions, wider options of courses to follow, more adventurous mixes of subjects. Nevertheless, only in subjects where there is clear indication of secure employment prospects and satisfactory salaries after graduation — veterinary science, medicine and pharmacy, for example — are courses significantly oversubscribed. In other subjects, even though there may be adequate career opportunities, prospective students are aware that financial rewards and social status are likely to be low.

All of the sciences, all branches of engineering, as well as medicine, surgery and all the orthodox paramedical subjects, can be studied at one or other of the London universities. This is not the place to rank the quality of the various departments and institutions: the government tries to do so from time to time, with results that bring vigorous protests from places not near the top of the list.

However, it would be wrong not to mention that several Nobel prizes have been won by members of the staff of Imperial, King's, and University Colleges, all constituent units of the University of London. Not all departments at these colleges, or at all other colleges and universities, can boast such eminence in the sciences.

Nevertheless, the exceptionally high quality of the scientific, engineering or medical endeavour recognized by these Nobel awards undoubtedly has an influence on neighbouring departments and institutions. This has encouraged a particularly high quality of teaching in these subjects in London, helping to make the universities of London a magnet for students from Britain and the whole world.

MEDICAL EDUCATION

Independently of the activities of the Universities of Oxford and Cambridge and centuries before the founding of the University of London, there had been a national need for the regulation from the capital of certain professional activities. The regulation of medical education took place long after similar control had been applied to the training of priests and lawyers.

In 1518, after receiving a petition requesting it, Henry VIII issued a charter founding the Royal College of Physicians. The petitioners, led by the court physician Thomas Linacre, the translator of Galen, wanted the new College to issue licences for medical practitioners. Initially, the power to do so applied only to a radius of seven miles round London, but within five years was extended to cover the whole country, though in parallel with licences granted by the universities.

From 1858, the licensing of medical practice within the kingdom passed to the

Opposite: Eighteenth-century engraving of the Royal College of Physicians in Warwick Lane, the location of the College from the late seventeenth century until 1825.

Right: Henry VIII with the Barber Surgeons, *by Hans Holbein the Younger (collection of the Royal College of Surgeons).*

General Medical Council (also situated in London) but the Royal College of Physicians continues to supervise the quality of medical training in the country's medical schools and training hospitals. In addition, it is responsible for various specialist examinations, for maintaining standards, for various publications, and for many other matters of professional concern. Furthermore, the College, now housed in an elegant new building in Regent's Park, maintains a fine historical library and a collection of portraits of former Presidents of the College.

Scriptural interpretation originally forbade invasion of the body, so physicians were tolerated by the church but surgeons were not. Surgery, however, even in the primitive conditions prevailing before the introduction of anaesthesia and asepsis, was evidently a necessity of life. Thus surgery was practised, despite the disapproval of the church, but in England the surgeons were originally associated with barbers. The historical remnant of this association is the traditional red and white striped pole outside barbers' shops, in which the red represented blood.

The barbers, with their recognized trade, formed a city guild in London. The sur-

A mid-eighteenth-century engraving of Gresham College, the former home of Sir Thomas Gresham in Bishopgate, the location of the College until 1768.

geons, still a trade rather than a profession, established the Barber-Surgeons Company or guild in 1540 (also by charter from Henry VIII) but it took more than 250 years before this company was able to evolve into the present Royal College of Surgeons, situated in Lincoln's Inn Fields. There, in a fine building restored after heavy bomb damage during the 1939-1945 war, the College houses the Hunterian and other museums, an extensive library, and an impressive portrait collection. The College has duties and responsibilities matching those of the physicians' college. In addition, it has given space to important research laboratories.

Alongside the physicians and surgeons, civilized life from early times required the services of apothecaries. A Society of Apothecaries was formed in London in 1617. From the sixteenth to the nineteenth centuries, apothecaries acted much as general practitioners. In consequence, there was considerable friction between the Society and the Royal College of Physicians. Although the Royal College had greater prestige, the apothecaries had two advantages: the protection of a city guild, established as the Company of Apothecaries in 1674, and the Society's own foundation in 1673 of the Chelsea Physic Garden, a major resource for teaching the virtues of medically important herbs even after the opening, 100 years later, of the Royal Botanic Gardens at Kew.

The Society thus survived as the authority for the education and licensing of apothecaries, whether acting as general practitioners or only as pharmacists. Eventually, the former became the responsibility of the General Medical Council and the latter of the Royal Pharmaceutical Society, founded in 1841 and now with premises in Lambeth High Street.

In the twentieth century, the developments within medicine and surgery have led to the establishment of other Royal Colleges, all with premises in London. These control the specialist education and examination of, respectively, Anaesthetists, General Practitioners,

Nursing, Obstetricians and Gynaecologists, Pathologists, Psychiatrists, and Radiologists. Other specialities which at present are organized as Faculties of one or other of the Royal Colleges of Physicians or Surgeons will probably be granted Royal College status of their own in due course.

OTHER ROYAL SCHOOLS AND COLLEGES

All members of society were interested in health and so benefitted from the establishment of organizations regulating the treatment of sickness and disease. Specialist groups and the government had more particular problems, which led to the foundation of specialist schools to deal with them. Farmers needed skilled care to maintain the health of their livestock. This led in 1791 to the foundation on land at Camden Town, then a country village, of the Royal Veterinary College. When the first graduates emerged from the College, the government realized that there was at last a body of men who could attend the army's horses, and for a while the

Students at work in the Dissection Room of the Royal Veterinary College, London, circa 1910.

main purpose of the College was diverted to the training of military veterinary surgeons. With the passage of time, however, the College regained its initial direction. In 1949 it became a constituent school of the University of London and now awards University of London degrees.

The main part of the College remains on its original site, but it has now expanded part of its activities to a 430 acre (175 ha) site at North Mymms, Hatfield, about twenty miles north of London. For graduates of this and other centres of veterinary teaching in the country, a Royal College of Veterinary Surgeons has been established in London, with a role similar to that of the medical Royal Colleges.

From the sixteenth and seventeenth centuries onwards, the government's increasing military requirements gave rise to the need for well-educated navigators, shipwrights and engineers to deal with naval and military equipment. The Royal Naval Dockyards were established at Woolwich in the early sixteenth century. Close to them, 100 years later, the Royal Laboratory was set up to develop new explosives. The whole site, of about 100 acres (45 ha), became the Royal Arsenal and on it was established in 1741 the Royal Military Academy. This became the most important centre of technical instruction in military science, mostly for army officers. The Academy moved to another site in Woolwich at the end of the eighteenth century, and out of London, to Sandhurst, in the middle of the twentieth.

In the mid-nineteenth century, Prince Albert was concerned that there were no specialists with the knowledge of chemistry required for solving national problems affecting agriculture, industry and medicine. As a result, in 1845, the Royal School of Chemistry was established at 16 Hanover Square. After a few years, it amalgamated with the Government School of Mines and the whole organization moved to South Kensington, on a site acquired with the proceeds of the Great Exhibition of 1851. Other institutions moved to the site over the next few decades and further re-organizations followed. The several schools were brought under the aegis of the University of London in 1895 and were merged to form Imperial College in 1907.

INFORMAL TEACHING AND STUDY CENTRES

The Royal College of Physicians, the Royal College of Surgeons and the Society of Apothecaries were established to deal with professional standards and qualifications. But the foundation (after several more centuries) of the University of London to provide a centre of teaching and research had already been preceded by a number of other institutions of higher learning.

Count Rumford, founder of the Royal Institution, in a cartoon by J. Gillray, 1801.

One of the most remarkable, covering the sciences and humanities, is Gresham College. Sir Thomas Gresham, a rich London merchant, by the terms of his will of 1579, endowed the foundation of the college which bears his name. From 1597, the College has appointed professors in the traditional subjects of European universities at the time of the Renaissance: astronomy, geometry, physic (i.e. medicine), rhetoric (in practice, grammar and logic), law, divinity and music. Each professor was to give four public lectures each year and these lectures have been delivered, as Gresham wished, for nearly 400 years.

The College was originally housed in Gresham's mansion, on a site now occupied by Liverpool Street Station. That building was appropriated by the City of London Corporation, following the Great Fire of 1666. After many moves in the interim, the College now has premises in Barnard's Inn, an elegant old building in a tiny courtyard off Holborn. Distinguished scholars still deliver the lectures specified by Gresham, with no admission charge to small but enthusiastic audiences.

Nearly three centuries after Gresham, as the industrial revolution began to gather pace in Britain, a realization grew that the country had need of educated and informed workmen to run the new machinery. For this purpose the Royal Society for

Left: Sketch from the
Illustrated London
News *of Faraday*
lecturing on
Magnetism and Light
at the Royal
Institution on 23
January 1846.

Below: The house of
the Royal Society of
Arts, John Adam
Street.

the Encouragement of Arts, Manufactures and Commerce was founded in 1754. In this title, 'art' meant technical artifice as well as the design of machine-made objects. During its early years, the Royal Society of Arts (RSA), as it is now generally known, provided lectures for mechanics and artisans on the practical applications of science.

After a few decades, however, the RSA lecture rooms became a fashionable resort for the aristocracy and rich middle-class families living in central London. Mechanics ceased to be welcome in the audiences at lectures which were less and less practically oriented. Nevertheless, the RSA eventually recovered its initial purposes. It still arranges lectures which lean to the arts in the modern sense; but it also plays an important part in technological education. Lectures dealing with industrial manufacture are given in the RSA building in John Adam Street, and also elsewhere in the country. An important function of the RSA is the supervision of examinations in subjects taught in technical and further education colleges throughout the land, issuing diplomas to successful candidates.

Just before the end of the eighteenth century, Benjamin Thompson, later Count

*The Coat of Arms of
the Royal Society
from the Society's
Charter Book.*

Rumford, established the Royal Institution of Great Britain for the Dissemination of Useful Knowledge. Thompson himself was a practically-minded scientist: he designed baffles to prevent a back-flow of air down chimneys and so to avoid filling rooms with smoke; and he demonstrated that friction produced heat, by recording the rise of temperature while boring cannon. His intention was that the Royal Institution (RI) would help educate mechanics in up-to-date technology.

Like the RSA, the RI became a fashionable rendezvous and the classes for mechanics were squeezed out. Fortunately, one mechanic, Michael Faraday, then an apprentice to a bookbinder, managed to attend lectures given by Humphrey Davy, an early professor at the RI. In 1813 Faraday persuaded Davy to accept him as a laboratory assistant. He eventually succeeded Davy on the latter's retirement and was one of the world's most productive and innovative scientists. Davy altered the emphasis of the RI's objectives from those laid down by Rumford so as to allow a greater concentration on scientific research. Over the two centuries of its existence, the laboratories of the RI have been the site of brilliant scientific discoveries under successive directors: after Davy and Faraday there were, among others, Tyndall, Dewar, Rayleigh, William and Lawrence Bragg, Porter and Thomas.

These discoveries — above all those of Faraday — have been of incalculable industrial importance and would surely have reconciled Rumford to the diversion of his original aims in founding the RI. However, lectures have continued to be given there. Those to the high society audiences of the early nineteenth century have now become the famous Friday Evening Discourses, still fashionable to the extent that the programme contains the rubric, 'while evening dress (dinner jacket) is not obligatory, the Council [of the RI] would like guests to know that it is customary.'

The RI also mounts the annual Christmas Lectures for children, now televised by the BBC and shown in Britain and abroad. In addition, the RI presents exciting lecture programmes for school audiences during term times, workshop sessions for school science teachers, seminars in the history of science, and many other educational activities.

The examples of the RSA and the RI led to the foundation of several similar organizations, both in central London and in the suburbs, which, early in the nineteenth century, may have been outlying villages. Some of these have long since expired: for example, the London Institution in Finsbury Circus, the Surrey Institution by Blackfriars Bridge, and the Russell Institution in Bloomsbury, all of which were founded in the first decade of the nineteenth century.

Others from that century have survived and are still very active. Examples are the Highgate Literary and Scientific Institution, founded in 1840, the Croydon Natural History and Scientific Society, founded in 1870, and the Hampstead Scientific Society, founded in 1899. Recent years have seen the foundation of the Merton Scientific Society (1945), the Richmond Scientific Society (1948) and the Bourne Society (1956), which has a group concerned with natural history in the Coulsdon and Purley areas. These societies typically hold regular weekly or monthly meetings through the autumn to spring months and maintain a loyal membership.

LEARNED SOCIETIES

Even the most distinguished establishments for teaching and research do not necessarily provide the most appropriate venue for specialists to discuss recent advances in their subject, as well as new ideas which have been floated. It was with this realization in mind that a group of men came to London from Oxford on 28 November 1660 to attend a lecture given at Gresham College by Christopher Wren, the Gresham Professor of Astronomy at that time. After the lecture, they all repaired to a local hostelry, probably the Bull's Head Tavern in Cheapside, and resolved to arrange regular meetings to discuss 'Physico-Mathematicall Experimentall Learning.' Eighteen months later, Charles II incorporated the group by royal charter as The Royal Society of London for Improving Natural Knowledge. Some earlier-founded societies with similar aims in other countries have since atrophied and vanished and the Royal Society remains the world's oldest-surviving general science society. Although it is in effect the national academy of sciences, the

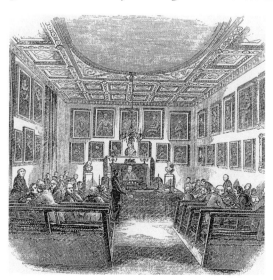

Royal Society is an independent body; it receives funds from the state, but is free of government control.

In its first few years, the Royal Society met at Gresham College. It later had various homes and in the nineteenth century the Society's

A nineteenth-century meeting of the Royal Society while it was at Somerset House.

offices were for a while at Somerset House in the Strand. These rooms are now occupied by the Courtauld Institute (where the Royal Society's name can nevertheless still be seen in the stonework over the door). For many years it was located at Burlington House in Piccadilly, alongside other scientific societies, before moving in 1965 to its present address in Carlton House Terrace. Since its inception, the Royal Society has been the venue for erudite meetings, at which scientists present and discuss the results of their latest researches.

From its earliest days, it has published records (*Transactions*) of these meetings together with communications sent in by contributors; and this type of journal publication has expanded considerably in this century. The Society has also published books from time to time, one of the first being Newton's *Principia Mathematica*. Beyond this, in its role as the national academy of sciences, the Society administers scholarships and travel funds, provides advice to the

The Royal Society of Medicine, Wimpole Street.

government on scientific matters when so requested, gives financial support to various scientific enterprises and conferences, corresponds and negotiates with foreign academies, and engages in the myriad other matters required in the management of modern science.

From its foundation to the present, the prestige of the Royal Society has always been at the highest level. This was in part due to the outstanding quality of its scientific Fellows (Hooke, Boyle and Wren were foundation Fellows and Newton was elected a few years later), and the eminence of its Presidents (among whom, before the middle of the nineteenth century, were Wren, Pepys, Newton himself, Sloane, Banks, and Davy).

But in addition, because the Society followed the precepts of Francis Bacon, whose writings had inspired its foundations, and often presented lectures accompanied by elaborate and entertaining demonstrations, it became, in the eighteenth century, one of the most fashionable clubs in London. Among the Fellows at that time, non-scientists came to outnumber the scientists. A movement for reform was initiated in the 1820s by Babbage, Brewster and John Herschel, but it took nearly fifty years for the Society to become a truly professional body, with only a few honorary Fellows, mostly members of the royal family and prime ministers.

Sir Joseph Banks was a highly conservative president of the Royal Society for forty-two years from 1778. He vigorously opposed the establishment of other scientific societies, lest there should be a diminution of the prestige of the Royal Society, which indeed covered then, as it still does, all the sciences. Nevertheless, after James Edward Smith had purchased the collection of animal and plant specimens and a large manuscript collection from the estate of Linnaeus, Banks was unable to prevent the formation of the Linnean Society in 1788 for biologists. Within a few years, however, other specialist groups were pressing for their own societies to be established, often with a royal patron, whom Banks was unable to oppose. Thus were established the Royal Society of Medicine (1805), the Royal Entomological Society (1806), the Geological Society (1807), and the Royal Astronomical Society (1820), all of which were and still are based in London.

Of particular note are the professional societies established by engineers. These were the people who created the wealth and splendour of Victorian society. The Institution of Civil Engineers began as a coffee house group in 1818 but was granted a royal charter ten

years later and elected Thomas Telford, the renowned designer of canals, harbours, and bridges, as its first president. The Institution of Mechanical Engineers was founded in 1847 with George Stephenson (see p.173) as its first president. The established use of gas as a domes-

The Institution of Electrical Engineers, Savoy Place.

tic and industrial fuel led to the foundation in 1863 of the Institution of Gas Engineers. The Society of Telegraph Engineers, founded in 1871 and reflecting one of the commercially most important uses of electricity at that time, changed in 1888 to its present title, the Institution of Electrical Engineers, as the wider uses of electricity began to be realized. And by 1889, naval engineers felt themselves to be sufficiently different from naval architects to form the Institution of Marine Engineers.

NEW SOCIETIES

After Banks's resignation in 1820 as President of the Royal Society, the number of new scientific societies increased rapidly and the increase continued for more than 150 years. Most of the new societies were based in London. In the past decade, however, the rise has slowed down as increasing administrative costs and higher rents have forced many societies either to amalgamate with others or to move out of London.

There is no central register in England of learned societies. Nor is it possible to trace definitively all the specialist training centres that continually spring up to deal with types of alternative medicine, aspects of information technology (especially computer programming), particular engineering techniques, and so on. As the twentieth century draws to a close, it appears that there are around twelve universities in London, about 200 hundred learned societies dealing with specialities in science, medicine or engineering, and perhaps 200 unattached teaching centres offering diplomas in various particular parts of these areas of knowledge.

The Library of the Royal Society.

CHAPTER 3
WHERE THE WORK IS DONE
Libraries and Laboratories

The books came first. Save for the misguided work of the alchemists and the studies in the modern scientific manner of William Gilbert on magnetism and electrification, there was not much experimental science done in Britain before the writings of Francis Bacon (1561-1626). Bacon's arguments led the founders of the Royal Society to encourage experimentation (see p.125), but they began to collect books immediately and, as a result, the Society's library has a particularly rich collection. However, the Royal Society library, like the even older though more specialized collection at the Royal College of Physicians (see pp.119,135), is private, so that access to it is limited.

PUBLIC ACCESS LIBRARIES
The pre-eminent public science library in London was formerly known as the Patent Office Library, established in 1885. In 1982 it became the Science Reference and Information Service (SRIS) of the British Library.

Because of the vast amount of paper now generated in the publication of science, space requirements have forced this library in recent years to divide into two parts. The main part, in Southampton Buildings, Holborn, contains books and journals relating to the physical sciences and technologies and engineering, and also British and foreign patents, trademarks, and business information. The other section, in Kean Street, Aldwych, has books and journals relating to the life sciences and technologies, mathematics, astronomy and earth sciences.

The SRIS has the world's largest collection of patents — thirty-three million of them — as well as a quarter of a million books, subscriptions to over 25,000 current journals, and thousands of company reports, catalogues and house journals. Particularly remarkable of the Holborn branch is that all the stacks and shelves are on open access. There is space only for the journals of the last decade, but the pleasure of being able to reach all the rare texts amply compensates.

The SRIS deals mostly with current science, even though it has that large stock of older materials. It is part of the British Library, which in turn has several branches in London and elsewhere in the country. The British Library was formed as an amalgamation of several libraries and services, but undoubtedly the most prestigious section of it is what was once called the British Museum Library.

This enormous collection began when the museum was founded in 1753 by the acquisition for the nation of collections of books, manuscripts, coins, antiquities and natural history specimens assembled by Sloane, Cotton, and Harley. Sloane's collection, in particular, contained several thousand medical and scientific books. And in the following two centuries the library acquired by its copyright privilege all the books published in the UK in these areas, as well as those foreign publications which it purchased.

As a result, the British Museum section of the British Library is the ultimate resource for much study into the history of science, medicine and engineering. However, access to this library requires you to obtain a Reader's Ticket, and then to request a book which must be fetched by a porter from the book stacks. It is a library only for serious research, not for casual use.

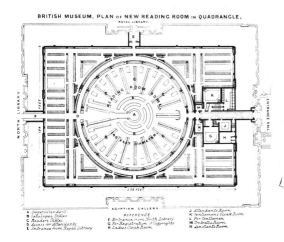

Front and back of the invitation card to a private view of the British Museum Reading Room on 5ᵗʰ May 1857.

Another major library of current science, with free access to members of the public, is the Science Museum Library. This was once within the Science Museum, but having outgrown its space, it moved into a building on the Imperial College site, adjacent to the

Lyon Playfair and the Haldane Libraries of Imperial College. In 1992 the three libraries were merged and now offer very high-level specialized science to the public as well as to the staff and students of the College.

A number of other science libraries in London, or science collections within general libraries, are fully public in the sense that anyone can enter at any time during opening hours and consult any of the books in stock. Most of these are the libraries under the auspices of the London boroughs which, in principle, have an arrangement between themselves for distributing specialities.

Thus, for example, Croydon specializes in computing and has a collection of about 5,000 volumes in this area. Ealing specializes in electrical engineering and Harrow in civil engineering. Westminster, in the Marylebone library, has an important medical and health science collection of 41,000 volumes and subscribes to 150 current journals.

However, the local government councils, which control these libraries, have suffered severe financial constraints in recent years. In consequence, the libraries have been unable, in most cases, to keep their collections up to date.

The Ciba Foundation.
Portland Place.

PRIVATE COLLECTIONS

Apart from the libraries funded by the government or local councils for public use, there are a few privately owned collections which are specifically offered as a public facility. Frederick Horniman, by whose philanthropy the museum that bears his name was established (see p.40), also specified in his will that the library of the museum should be freely open to the public. The library of 25,000 volumes provides an excellent back-up to the subjects dealt with in the museum displays: biology and natural history, ethnography, and music.

The Ciba Foundation, in Portland Place, was founded by the Swiss pharmaceutical company in 1947 primarily for 'promoting international co-operation in medical, chemical, biological and pharmaceutical research.' It does so by arranging lectures and symposia, held in the conference room at the rear of the house. The Foundation also houses an attractive library for the use of scientists staying in its guest rooms, but which is open for use by visitors who can claim some professional interest in the topics covered by the library's holdings. The technical books and journals in the library deal with medicine, surgery and the basic medical sciences. In addition, the library has acquired the Oppenheimer collection of (mostly) medical biographies, which is kept up to date with new purchases.

Of libraries established by charitable bequest and freely accessible to members of the public, the most notable are those at the Wellcome Centre (see p.112), which specializes in the biomedical sciences. The Information Service on the upper ground floor offers an excellent collection of reference material about science policy, teaching resources, and current science news. It also provides access via computers to various science databases. There is a medical photographic library with about 100,000 photographs of medical historical material, about half of which can be accessed by a videodisc system, and a biomedical video library. In the same building, the Library of the Wellcome Institute for the History of Medicine is Europe's leading centre for the study of its speciality.

The library of the Wellcome Institute for the History of Medicine.

A library that must be added to this account, even though it is accessible only by prior appointment, is that of the Natural History Museum. It is enormous, and is generally considered to have the best natural history collection in the world. In the collection are a million volumes and 20,000 serial runs of journals, about half of them current. The library is arranged in a number of separate sections, dealing respectively with botany, zoology, entomology, earth sciences (i.e. palaeontology, mineralogy, meteorology, etc.), and general science. There is also an archive collection and an ornithology branch of the library in the museum's outstation at Tring. The Librarians will grant admittance only to *bona fide* research workers, and only to those who need resources not available in their local public or academic libraries.

There is also a leading botanical library at the Royal Botanic Gardens, Kew. This holds 120,000 books, as well as many journals, manuscripts, illustrations and an extensive archive.

ACADEMIC CENTRES

The academic centres in London are private institutions in legal terms, but the libraries of nearly all of them are semi-public. That is to say, members of the public can apply to the Librarian for a Reader's Ticket (for which there is sometimes a charge) and will then be allowed to use the library for a limited period. The universities are largely supported by government funds and so have to some extent a public presence. The learned societies are financed only by their members and in general are entirely private. Nevertheless, some of them have a policy of making their libraries semi-public in the same way as the universities do.

Left: Students at work in the library of Birkbeck College, University of London.

Below right: The library of the Royal Institution in a print by Rowlandson and Pugin, 1809.

Of university libraries, the amalgamation of that at Imperial College with the Science Museum Library has already been mentioned. The combined libraries make a splendid science information centre for the west of London. Apart from the extensive collection of books and journals, access to the major science databases is available through computer-controlled monitor screens.

There is another large and compact university science library in London with similar facilities. It is sited at University College, but is named the Bloomsbury Science Library and combines the collections of several colleges and institutes of the University of London in the Bloomsbury area. King's College also holds a large science collection, but at present it is split between three sites.

There are very useful, but smaller, general collections at the other colleges of the University of London and at the other London universities. The specialized university centres in the city, such as the medical schools and the various medical and other research institutes of the University of London (for example, Archaeology, Cancer, Dental Surgery, Ophthalmology) all have correspondingly specialized libraries. These are usually made accessible to members of the public on the same basis as the other academic libraries.

LEARNED SOCIETIES

The learned societies do not all maintain libraries. Most of those more than a century old do, but most less than fifty years old do not. And when the libraries do exist, they are usually specialized to the interests of the society.

In all cases where non-members may be admitted, this can be arranged only through prior application to the Librarian. Admission is rarely refused if the applicant can show why use of that particular library is necessary.

The Linnean Society has a very open policy of admission to its distinguished biological science library of about 90,000 volumes. The Institute of Petroleum, which has its library housed in particularly beautiful rooms with classically painted ceilings, is also very positive in accepting non-member visitors, although on payment of a small fee.

The Royal Astronomical Society has a library at Burlington House, which admits non-members by prior arrangement with the Librarian, but is not prepared to deal with applicants whose primary interest is in astrology. The Royal Society of Chemistry, also at Burlington House, has a particularly fine library of chemical sciences. It operates the same admission policy by prior appointment as that just mentioned, but non-members can gain immediate admission if they can provide an appropriate letter of introduction from a member. Furthermore, members can take out books on loan, but this is not allowed for non-members.

The libraries of the major engineering institutions have similar arrangements. They all have comprehensive libraries of their subject, with important holdings of books and journals. In addition, these institutions, particularly the Electrical Engineers and the Civil Engineers, hold large archive collections, of great historical importance.

There are two other libraries that must be mentioned, since they have admission policies for visitors like those of the institutions just listed, and they are situated in ancient, though not strictly professional, organizations. At the Royal Institution, the library covers all of science. It has a substantial historical section, including early volumes of publications of foreign scientific academies. The modern holdings are strongest in physical chemistry, the main area of research over the past few decades of the people in the Davy-Faraday Laboratories of the RI. It also has good collections of serious popular science works and of scientific biographies.

The RSA (Royal Society of Arts — see p.123) has for many years concentrated on design in all categories of products, but especially of manufactured goods. Its library, in its beautiful Adam building in the Adelphi, is small but has a useful collection of books and papers concerned with contemporary design, with education in this area, and with the relationship of industry and education and training. The RSA offers non-members a year's library ticket for a modest charge.

MEDICAL LIBRARIES

London is especially rich in medical libraries. Those of the medical schools, and of the medical research institutes attached to the University of London, as well as that of the Marylebone branch of the Westminster Public Library, have been mentioned before. The London Hospital Medical School has recently found spectacular accommodation in the building that was formerly the church of St Augustine with St Peter, on the hospital site. The Guy's branch of the United (St Thomas's and Guy's) Medical School, thanks to an Edwardian benefaction, has a very elegant cased library. And the Royal Free Hospital School of Medicine has a library housed in a light and airy modern building.

However, leading all the medical libraries in both size and coverage is that of the Royal Society of Medicine. This magnificent collection contains about half a million volumes and carries subscriptions to approximately 2,000 journals. As with the libraries of other professional institutions, a letter of introduction from a member (Fellow) is required for a non-member to be allowed use of the library; but the temporary ticket then provided is not renewable and allows only five visits to the library within a month of issue. Alternatively, a non-member who can make a case could purchase temporary membership.

Another professional medical library is that of the British Medical Association. This also has a large collection and tends to specialize in current medical practice and matters of medical policy and politics. It has a particularly efficient arrangement of lending and providing information such as research reports to members outside London and to other professional institutions. Non-members need an introduction from an associated institutional library, or may purchase a day Reader's Ticket, but this is relatively expensive.

Each of the royal colleges has a notable library. The Library at the Royal College of Surgeons, for example, has a particularly rich collection of books and journals relating to all types of surgery, including dental surgery. The library of the Royal College of Physicians is now limited to

Left: The Royal College of Surgeons, Lincoln's Inn Fields, in 1828.

Right: The Guy's Hospital buildings of the United Medical and Dental Schools.

the history of medicine, complementing and supplementing the library of the Wellcome Institute for the History of Medicine. The Obstetricians and Gynaecologists have recently refurbished their library, providing a comfortable location for researchers or students preparing for examinations. This, indeed, is the case for the libraries of all the royal colleges, large and small.

The libraries mentioned in this account are the most significant to which people can gain admittance to consult works of general scientific, medical or engineering relevance. However, except for those that are explicitly designated as public libraries, the intending visitor who is not a member of the organization maintaining the library is advised to write or telephone beforehand to check the conditions of admission. And apart from these libraries, there are countless strictly private ones. Many university departments maintain specialist collections of this sort. So do some professional societies.

LABORATORIES AND THEIR FUNDING

The books came first but are perhaps now on their way out, to be replaced by microfiches and electronic data communication. The output of the laboratories has radically changed the world over the past century. That change will continue if the laboratory scientists and engineers can find sufficient funds to continue their work.

The largest source of research funds is the government and it is appropriate to summarize the governmental organization of scientific research. Although the Government's policy is to leave industry to follow its own research interests, research in the universities depends crucially on government funding. The funds are channelled to university laboratories, independent agencies and, very occasionally, to industrial companies through research councils. These were re-organized and renamed in 1993 as the Engineering & Physical Science, Particle Physics & Astronomy, Biotechnology & Biology, Natural Environment, Economics & Social, and Medical Research Councils. They are joined in an organization supervised by a Director General of Research Councils and come under the authority of the government minister who directs the Office of Science and Technology.

The policies of the research councils have moved towards urging academic research workers to collaborate with industrial companies. The Department of Trade and Industry (DTI) encourages this collaboration and contributes to the cost of many such collaborative programmes. The DTI is also the government department directly responsible for several major executive agencies and laboratories such as the National Physical Laboratory, the Laboratory of the Government Chemist, and the National Weights and Measures Laboratory.

THE FIRST LABORATORIES

It was not always so. Laboratories were places in which, when the word was first used, only chemists worked. And the chemists' laboratories developed out of the alchemists' kitchens. Dr John Dee, an Elizabethan mathematician and astronomer, was also an astrologer and alchemist. In 1564 he was appointed royal adviser in mystic secrets, including alchemy. Instruments he used in his kitchen-cum-laboratory are in the British Museum collection.

For more than 200 years thereafter, laboratories for the most part remained as rooms in private houses. An exception was the Royal Laboratory established at Woolwich in 1695 where skilled chemists were expected to manufacture explosives and to develop new and better ones. The remains of this building are now absorbed within the Royal Arsenal.

Opposite: a view circa *1750 of the buildings of the Royal Laboratory in Laboratory Square, The Royal Arsenal.*

Right: Dr Dee's obsidian mirror with its leather carrying case, in the collection of the British Museum.

Among the important private laboratories were those set up for the chemist Joseph Priestley (1733-1804) when he was tutor to the household of Lord Shelburne. One was in the family's London home, Lansdowne House in Berkeley Square, and the other at the country seat, Bowood, near Calne in Wiltshire. In these, Priestley pursued the researches that led to the discovery of oxygen. At about the same time, Henry Cavendish (1731-1810) arranged a laboratory in his country house at Clapham (now well within London) where he discovered hydrogen, and the hydrogen-oxygen composition of water, and made important studies into electricity and gravitation.

A more recently used private laboratory was that at Avenue House, East End Road, Finchley, originally the home of Dr Henry Stephens (1796-1864) who developed a suspension of carbon particles which he marketed as Stephen's Ink. His son Henry, universally known as 'Inky' Stephens (1841-1918), maintained the laboratory to improve the inks produced by his company. He left his house and gardens to the people of the Borough of Finchley as a museum and park. The laboratory was destroyed by fire in 1989, but a small exhibition of pens, nibs, inkpots and copperplate script is on display (open Tue-Thur, 14.00-16.30). No doubt, too, many other scientists over the centuries found space at home to accommodate the apparatus needed for their studies.

At the semi-private level, the Royal Society promoted experimentation from its inception and experimental demonstrations were given at its early meetings. Its first accommodation was in Gresham College and no doubt a room was assigned to Robert Hooke, its first 'curator of experiments' as a laboratory for developing them. However, with the passage of time and the establishment of laboratories elsewhere, experimentation ceased in

the premises of the Royal Society and the Fellows and their guests resorted there just to report their results.

In a strict sense, the oldest science research centre that survives in London is the work-room of John Flamsteed. This has now been turned into a museum, the Old Royal Observatory at Greenwich (see p.79). The Octagon Room there and the models of the type of telescope with which Flamsteed worked, the chronometers he used and one of his

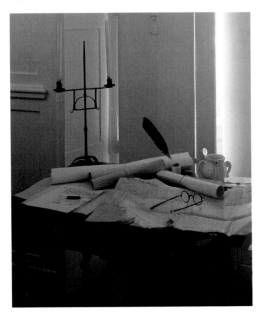

Above: Nineteenth-century watercolour of Faraday at work in his laboratory at the Royal Institution.

Left: Flamsteed's desk at the Old Royal Observatory, Greenwich.

Opposite: Undergraduate students in a physics laboratory class at University College London.

quadrants, give a clear idea of the method of astronomical research at the end of the seventeenth century. Other displays at the museum show how this research developed in the succeeding 250 years.

The earliest research laboratory to have survived to the present is that at the Royal Institution. It was here that Humphrey Davy first isolated potassium, sodium, calcium, chlorine and other elements and here also that he did the work that led to his invention of the miner's lamp. He was followed by Michael Faraday whose astonishing series of studies and discoveries, including the composition of benzene, the liquefaction of gases, the laws of electrolysis, electromagnetic induction, and magneto-optic phenomena, were all made in the rooms that today form the Faraday Museum (see p.34) at the RI. Research at the RI has now been moved into other rooms, known collectively as the Davy-Faraday Laboratories.

UNIVERSITY LABORATORIES
The rise of the modern research laboratories began in the universities. Although earlier professorial chairs were established in Scotland, the first chairs in experimental science subjects were established in England at University College on its foundation as the original part of the University of London in 1828. Initially the professors at University College, King's College, and later the other colleges, were allotted only miniscule rooms for pursuing their researches. Gradually, however, these expanded, especially after the economic and financial advantages of science began to be appreciated and the science departments began to attract outside funds.

Science and scientific research laboratories were firmly established in the University of London by the end of the nineteenth century. All the science subjects in the University were significantly augmented by the establishment in 1907 of Imperial College of Science and Technology, an amalgamation of the Royal School of Mines (which itself had earlier absorbed the Royal College of Chemistry) and the Royal College of Science. Three years later the City and Guilds College also became part of Imperial College.

These and the other colleges, medical schools, and specialized research institutes of the University of London have a particularly distinguished record of scientific research. Within the many constituent schools and institutions of the university (approximately fifty in all) are laboratories covering very nearly every aspect of experimental science, medicine and engineering, as well as departments dealing with mathematics, theoretical physics and chemistry, computer science, information engineering, and so on.

Over the years, about twenty of the University's researchers have won Nobel prizes and these cover all the categories of science for which the prizes are awarded. The number of these prizewinners is given here approximately since some were at the University before the award, some after, and some were in post at the time the award was given for work done elsewhere. Imperial College claims the largest share of the Nobel laureates, followed by University and King's Colleges.

The other universities within London are too new yet to be able to claim such a distinguished record. Nevertheless, they contain active and important research laboratories. Of particular note are those at Brunel University, City University, and the Universities of East London, Middlesex, North London, and Westminster.

Left: Microscopic examination at the Central Public Health Laboratory of cell cultures infected with rubella *virus.*

Right: The National Institute for Medical Research, Mill Hill.

Below right: A scientist at the National Physical Laboratory making high accuracy measurements in an anechoic chamber of horn antennas, needed for the calibration of antennas carried in space by satellites.

The universities' laboratories and research centres are private places, into which the public is not generally admitted. An exception, however, is the University of London Observatory at Mill Hill (33 Daws Lane, NW7, 081-959 0421). Short tours are arranged for visitors at 18.30 and 19.30 on the first and third Friday of winter months during term times, to demonstrate the work of the Observatory. Terms run from 1 October to mid-December and from early January to the end of March, but intending visitors should telephone beforehand. Admission is generally free, but contributions are appreciated.

MEDICAL AND PUBLICLY-FUNDED RESEARCH

Many London hospitals that are not directly connected with a university, notably Northwick Park Hospital in Harrow and Harefield Hospital in Uxbridge, are important centres of medical research. Research and development at the latter have made it one of the world's leading places for heart transplant surgery. The main research effort at Northwick Park Hospital has been funded by the Medical Research Council (MRC) in the Clinical Research Centre there, although this will soon be moving to premises at the Hammersmith Hospital.

Among laboratories concentrating on research in the medical sciences, special mention must be made of the National Institute for Medical Research at Mill Hill. The Institute was established in 1913 by the MRC and was formerly sited at Holly Hill, Hampstead. In the course of the eighty-year history of the Institute, work done by the staff in its laboratories has attracted no less than four Nobel prizes and many other prestigious international awards. The Institute's research programme involves studies of the biomedical sciences, including developmental biology, genetics, immunology, parasitology, virology, biochemistry, neurobiology, neurophysiology, and neuropharmacology.

The nation's principal reference centre for medical microbiology is the Central Public Health Laboratory at Colindale. This laboratory, with 400 medical, scientific and support

staff, provides specialist expertise and advice to hospitals, government and industry around the country. Its research work concerns the micro-organisms that cause infectious disease — their origin, how they spread, and how they can be detected. Two particularly noteworthy early discoveries were that of the dog distemper virus (and the development of a vaccine), and that of the human influenza virus.

Other important laboratories dealing with fundamental medical problems and independent of the universities and governmental control are those of the Imperial Cancer Research Fund in Lincoln's Inn Fields. The laboratories of the Ludwig Institute for Cancer Research are also administratively and financially independent, although their directors have chosen to site them together with medical schools to gain advantage from the academic contacts.

In addition, the Royal National Institutes for, respectively, the Blind and the Deaf have laboratories of great value to the communities they serve. They test products brought to the market by manufacturers, as well as developing new products to help meet the disabilities of loss of sight or hearing.

Three major government executive agencies have laboratories situated at Teddington in west London. The longest-established tenant of the site is the National Physical Laboratory (NPL), founded in 1900. This acts as the standards laboratory for the UK. The scientists at the NPL also are actively involved in the development of new methods of measurement. In pursuing this work the staff cover a wide range of techniques in physics including applications in optics, acoustics, radiation science, electrical science and computer and information technology.

The NPL was joined at Teddington in 1988 by the Laboratory of the Government Chemist (LGC). The LGC was set up by the Board of Excise in 1854 to detect adulteration in tobacco, but has developed in parallel with the growth of technology in society. Its work is now mostly in applications of analytical chemistry and microbiological measurement, for control of food products and the environment, for ensuring health and safety standards, for monitoring trade goods, both imported and exported, and in forensic analysis.

Calorimeter and associated equipment at the Fire Research Station, used to measure heat and gaseous emission from burning materials.

The third executive agency on the Teddington site is the National Weights and Measures Laboratory (NWML), set up following the passage of the Weights and Measures Act 1985 and EU Directives on measuring instruments. The NWML provides type approval for any new trade equipment that dispenses or measures substances and also assesses suitability for use. Thus the NWML can give approval to new types of petrol pumps, beer meters, supermarket scales, railway weighbridges, and so on.

Several major public institutions and services run laboratories that have a specific aim related to the work of the institution. The Royal Botanic Gardens, Kew, include two major research facilities. The Herbarium contains the most comprehensive reference collection in the world of dried plants and fungi, with over six million specimens, used for the naming and classification of plants from all countries. The Jodrell Laboratory is a leading research centre for studying the structure, biochemistry and

*Left: Tensile strain
and breaking tests
being carried out on
train seat fabrics in
the laboratories of the
Scientific Services
Division of London
Underground.*

*Below: A research
scientist at work on a
micropropagation trial
in the Jodrell
Laboratories, Kew.*

genetics of plants, for isolating possible new
drugs from plants, and for seeking other economic exploitation of the plant world.

Other institutions have a need for testing
or analysis, rather than the development of
new methods or the discovery of new scientific facts, although often the one activity runs
into the other. Both the British Museum and
the National Gallery have laboratories that
command a wide range of scientific skills:
chemical and physical analysis, precise dating
of both ancient and modern artefacts, conservation, and environmental control. In these
instances, the research is advanced by the
results of analysis which can determine age,
provenance, and other important details.

Chemical and physical analysis, and precise dating, also play a large part in the work
of the Metropolitan Police Forensic Science

Laboratory (MPFSL) in Lambeth; here the analysis extends to biochemical determinations involved in blood grouping and DNA 'fingerprinting' from microscopic amounts of material, as well as image analysis of marks and prints left by tools, shoes, car tyres and so on, at the scene of crime.

At a lower level of crime than is dealt with by the MPFSL, but contributing greatly to the quality of the environment of Londoners, is the work of the Scientific Services Laboratory of London Underground in developing methods of removing graffiti which

have been applied with ever more durable materials. This laboratory also has the task of monitoring the lubricants, paints, fabrics and other materials used in the trains, as well as ensuring a safe and tolerable environment in respect of fumes, lighting, noise levels and safety in the several hundred miles of underground tracks, tunnels and stations.

The Fire Research Station (FRS) at Borehamwood is also concerned with people's safety. This laboratory is a branch of the Buildings Research Establishment situated outside London, at Watford. Its task is to develop new materials, or treatments of old materials, which might reduce flammability and consequent fire risk. Another responsibility of the FRS is to monitor the design of all objects, from large buildings to small electrified devices, that carry any chance of going up in flames or of causing a fire, and to alert manufacturers to an obligation of reducing fire risk.

COMMERCIAL LABORATORIES

In former years there were many large research laboratories in London run by industrial manufacturers and producers. In the last few decades, however, the high costs of any metropolitan operation, as well as the consequences of company amalgamations and re-organizations, have abolished most of them, or led to their removal to the provinces.

There are two major industrial research laboratories left in London devoted to physical science, electronics, and engineering. One is the Hirst Laboratory of GEC, in

Wembley but in the process of moving to Borehamwood. Here the main emphasis is on electric power transmission and machinery, although other research topics are communications systems and materials developments, especially of semiconductor compounds. The other is run by Thorn-EMI as its Central Research Laboratories at Hayes. Here the emphasis is on electronics applied to domestic devices, especially in relation to sound and sight reproduction and to computerized control devices.

Two other laboratories in this area deserve mention. One is run by the Sira Group at Chislehurst. Sira was formerly the Scientific Instrument Research Association, supported jointly by government and industry. When governmental support was withdrawn, the research association reconstituted itself as a successful group of companies specializing in the development and application of advanced systems of measurement, instrumentation, and control for the defence, manufacturing, aerospace, and other industries.

The second is run by British Maritime Technology Ltd (BMT) on a former part of the National Physical Laboratory (NPL) site at Teddington. BMT maintains water tanks and wind tunnels for trials of ship and structural models and offers research and consultancy facilities.

Opposite: A ship-towing tank in British Maritime Technology's major tank-testing facilities at Teddington.

Right: The Central Research Laboratories of Thorn-EMI at Hayes.

Apart from the electrical goods manufacturers, the only commercial companies retaining large laboratories within the boundaries of London are those of the pharmaceutical industry. Several large pharmaceutical laboratories have, indeed, moved from London since the 1970s. There remain the important laboratories of the Glaxo, Rhône-Poulenc (May & Baker) and Wellcome companies at Greenford, Dagenham, and Beckenham, respectively. In each case, the work of the scientists at these laboratories is to synthesize new products of medicinal value and to determine routes of their preparation. The chemical engineering concerned with the manufacture of the resulting drugs is done elsewhere.

There is no space here to mention the myriad small commercial laboratories or research groups that also flourish in London. These deal with all aspects of the technology of modern western European life. There are particularly large numbers of these dealing with the development of computers, covering both software and hardware, and also with production methods for materials of use in new biotechnology processes. At the end of the twentieth century, there is high-quality practical science, medicine and engineering flourishing in London and with more than adequate library and information resources to back it up.

CHAPTER 4
WORKS OF ART
Science Through the Artists' Eyes

Painters, working out of a tradition that concentrated on biblical, mythological and historical themes, responded with hesitation to possibilities of using science in their images. Indeed, only in the past 100 years or so have they begun to make systematic use of Newton's demonstrations of the colour composition of white light. Understandably, the confrontations of Greek gods or of generals on the field of battle offered more immediately dramatic pictures than scientists battling to uncover the secrets of Nature. The entry of painters to the world of science was with the practitioners rather than through the subject itself.

If a portrait painter were offered a commission, he or she would take it, whatever the profession of the sitter. As a result, there are some beautiful pictures and busts of scientists, engineers, physicians and surgeons in the National Portrait Gallery (NPG), the premises of the Royal College of Physicians, the Royal Society, the Royal Institution, the Royal College of Surgeons, and similar learned and academic institutions. Some of the greatest British painters and sculptors are represented in these collections, showing the faces of people, some of whom have names familiar to the public (Newton, Darwin, Wedgwood), others remembered only by their professional successors (Banks, Priestley, Rennie), and still others now forgotten by all.

NATIONAL PORTRAIT GALLERY

The NPG is such a treasure-house of science-in-art that it earns space of its own. The pictures for the most part are arranged chronologically, many grouped by the sitters' occupations. As a result, most of the portraits of scientists are to be found in Rooms 14, 16, 27 and 34 — the first two showing people of the eighteenth and nineteenth centuries, and the last two showing people of the twentieth century. However, the pictures in the other rooms should not be overlooked.

Opposite: Portrait of Sir Isaac Newton by Sir Godfrey Kneller, 1702 (National Portrait Gallery).

Right: Portrait of Dorothy Hodgkin by Maggi Hambling, 1985 (National Portrait Gallery).

Of the portraits normally on public display (many more are in the reserve collection and there is occasional rotation), about 120 are of men of science, engineering or medicine. Only four women are represented in these professional categories: an exciting painting by Maggi Hambling of Dorothy Hodgkin, winner of the Nobel Prize for her crystallographic studies, at work in her office, and one of Janet Vaughan, pathologist and former principal of Somerville College, Oxford [both in Room 34]; a portrait of Marie Stopes, the palaeobotanist and birth control pioneer [Room 27]; and a medallion of Mary Somerville, a mathematician who gave her name to Somerville College [Room 14].

The first major scientist encountered by the visitor exploring the Gallery systematically is Newton, in Room 4, portrayed by Godfrey Kneller and wearing a somewhat supercilious expression. Kneller also painted the portrait in Room 6 of Sir Christopher Wren, who should be remembered as an astronomer (one-time Professor of Astronomy at Gresham College in London) as well as the architect of St Paul's Cathedral. Close to Wren hang portraits of Halley, the astronomer and identifier of the comet that bears his name; Mead, a pre-eminent eighteenth-century physician; and Hales, a pioneer physiologist who demonstrated the rise of sap in plants and measured blood pressure by fitting a vertical

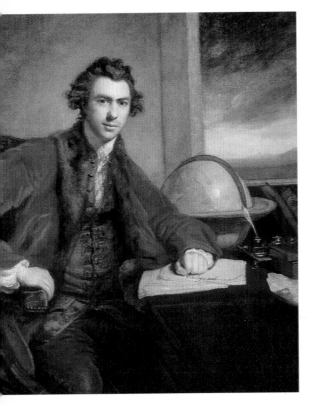

tube into the carotid artery of a horse and noting how far up the tube the blood rose.

In Room 11 there is a colourful portrait by Joshua Reynolds of the young Sir Joseph Banks, botanical collector, creator of the Royal Botanic Gardens at Kew and longest-ever serving President of the Royal Society (42 years, 1778-1820). He is seen soon after his return from the antipodes where he had sailed with Captain Cook. Cook was himself a considerable botanist, later a Fellow of the Royal Society, and his picture hangs on the adjacent wall. Also in Room 11, in one of the cases, and alongside some miniatures of other people with scientific connections, is an interesting terracotta plaque of Benjamin Franklin.

In that part of the NPG, it is also worth looking at two fine portraits in Rooms 9 and 10. One, another masterwork by Reynolds, is of a leading archaeologist, Fellow of the Royal Society, British Consul at Naples, whose name is best remembered through his wife: the picture is of Sir William Hamilton, married to Emma, the mistress of Admiral Lord Nelson. The other is a particularly engaging and sympathetic study by William Hogarth of a now totally forgotten mathematician, Dr William Jones, the effect of whose work, however, is known to every schoolchild: it was Jones who introduced the symbol π for the ratio of the circumference to the diameter of a circle.

The concentration of portraits of scientists and engineers in Rooms 14 and 16 has been mentioned and there are too many to give accounts of them here. Some, indeed, such as the paintings of Darwin (by John Collier) and Faraday (by Thomas Phillips), and the photograph by Julia Cameron of John Herschel, are widely known from their frequent appearance in books and even in advertisements. But in these rooms the busts and medallions should not be overlooked. And in Room 27 the cartoon of the astronomer James Jeans will be appreciated by all who have read his books of popular science. Among the modern pictures is a distinguished portrait of Bertrand Russell, the mathematician, logician and philosopher, by Roger Fry. Room 34 contains portraits of many eminent

Opposite: Portrait of Sir Joseph Banks by Sir Joshua Reynolds, 1773 (National Portrait Gallery).

Right: Cartoon by W. Heath Robinson, An Interesting And Elegant Apparatus Designed to Overcome Once For All The Difficulties of Conveying Peas to the Mouth *(National Museum of Cartoon Art).*

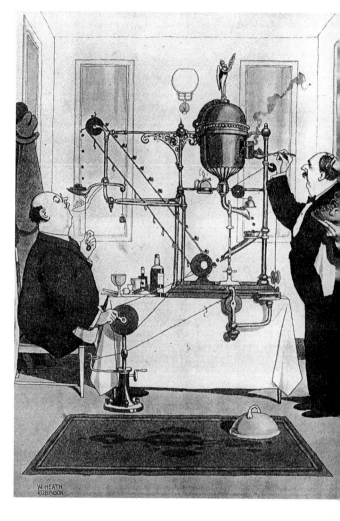

scientists, most of them still living, and the photographs and paintings include pictures of more than a dozen Nobel prizewinners.

SCIENCE IN CARTOON

Cartoonists occasionally show sympathy for their subjects, but have rarely done so for science or scientists. From the time of Gillray and Rowlandson in the late eighteenth century, science in cartoon has regularly been mocked or reviled. The drawings by Heath Robinson of bizarre imagined machines have made his name synonymous with gimcrack construction. Some of Robinson's pictures are displayed at the National Museum of Cartoon Art, where there are also examples of physical realizations of his imagined devices.

Cartoons by other artists typically show scientists as evil or mad, in the fashion of Hollywood. It is understandable that many recent cartoons to be seen in this museum are directed against war and thereby attack the technology and the technologists of war. Hardly ever does a cartoon show science in a positive light, or even portray its practitioners as attempting to do something creditable.

PORTRAITS IN CONTEXT

Portraits frequently indicate the painters' sympathy with and understanding of their subjects. It was a common custom of portrait painters of earlier times to paint into their pictures some items of the sitter's occupation. Thus admirals were often shown with telescopes in hand, architects with rulers or dividers, and field marshals with swords or cannon. To the extent that such objects might be called scientific instruments, pictures of this kind are called up by the computer search available at the Witt Library of the Courtauld Institute of Art of the University of London, when images of scientific interest are requested.

This practice is found to continue in many formal portraits of scientists, typically using one or two pieces of apparatus, or a book of which the sitter was the author, placed somewhere in the background. In the NPG portraits, a Tudor mathematician, Nicolaus Kratzer, tutor to the household of Sir Thomas More, is shown by a table carrying astrolabes and gnomons — he was a sundial specialist. Faraday is shown [NPG Room 16] against a bench on which stands an electric battery, T. H. Huxley [NPG Room 16], the biologist and disciple of Darwin, rests an arm against a pile of his books (he was a prolific author) and holds a primate skull (to deal with the 'missing link' controversy), Edward Jenner, discoverer of vaccination by using matter from cowpox blisters to inoculate against smallpox, is painted [NPG Room 14] sitting at a table which bears his book propped up against a cow's foreleg.

Exceptions that show a scientist actually at work are the portrait of Dorothy Hodgkin at the NPG, mentioned previously; the portrait by Paula McArthur at the NPG [Room 34] of Frederick Sanger, the Nobel prizewinning biochemist, in his laboratory; one at the Royal Society of Gowland Hopkins, the biochemist, at his laboratory bench, by Meredith

Left: Portrait of Sir Almroth Wright by Sir Gerald Kelly. 1934 (St Mary's Hospital Medical School).

Opposite: An Iron Forge by Joseph Wright of Derby 1772 (Tate Gallery).

Frampton; and at St Mary's Hospital Medical School (Committee Room) a sympathetic study by Gerald Kelly of Sir Almroth Wright at work. (Wright was a distinguished immunologist, the teacher of Alexander Fleming, and the original of Sir Colenso Ridgeon in G. B. Shaw's play, *The Doctor's Dilemma.*)

In some cases, the introduction of scientific instruments can, indeed, transform your impression of the picture. In the National Gallery, the outstanding masterpiece by Hans Holbein, *The Ambassadors*, [Nat Gal Room 2] shows two ambassadors from France to the court of Henry VIII, standing on either side of a two-tiered table with shelves bearing a large collection of globes, astrolabes, mirrors and other measuring devices. These, together with a distorted skull in the foreground, make the scene appear to be of lordly gentlemen in some mysterious scientific enterprise. Another great painting in this class at the same Gallery is *An Experiment on a Bird in the Air Pump* by Joseph Wright of Derby [Nat Gal Room 38]. A tutor is demonstrating to a family that creatures die in the absence of air and his apparatus in the centre of the canvas initially draws attention away from the mixed responses of his audience, some of whom react with horror, some with interest, and some with indifference.

IMAGES OF TECHNOLOGY

Wright (1734-1797) was one of the few painters before the present century who reacted positively to science and technology and used them in the scenes he painted. He was an associate of the Lunar Society of Lichfield whose members included James Watt and Matthew Boulton, the engineers, Josiah Wedgwood, the pottery manufacturer, Joseph Priestley, the chemist, and Erasmus Darwin. This Darwin, grandfather of Charles Darwin, was himself a distinguished physician and biologist and Fellow of the Royal Society, and his portrait by Wright hangs in the NPG [NPG Room 14]. A dramatic painting by Wright, recently acquired by the Tate Gallery, is *The Iron Forge* [Tate Room 3], showing the ironmaster and his assistants illuminated by the glow of white-hot metal, with his wife and child as surprising onlookers of the forging process.

The drama of engineering manufacture seems not to have been picked up again by painters until quite recent times. An epic example of this theme is the series of paintings by Stanley Spencer at the Imperial War Museum, *Shipbuilding on the Clyde* [Imp War, Ground Floor Gallery]. These works were commissioned by the War Artists Advisory Committee in 1940 and the following years as a record of the civilian contribution to the war effort. Spencer succeeded brilliantly in combining the spectacle of very large-scale manufacturing activity and the associated technology with an elevating depiction of the engineers and craftsmen of the Glasgow yard.

A drama of a very different sort, medical and distressing, is to be seen in an adjacent painting, *Gassed*, by John Singer Sargent. It shows a line of soldiers, blinded by the poison gas used on the battlefields of the First World War, being led to a treatment tent, each man guided by placing his hand on the shoulder of the man in front of him.

ART MEETS COMBAT

War and the clash of arms have always provided opportunities for artists as well as scientists. The British Museum has great stone bas reliefs in which Hittite and Assyrian sculptors celebrated the power of their armies and displayed their chariots and weapons [BM Rooms 17, 19-22] centuries before Archimedes (perhaps) turned his burning mirrors against the sails of the invading Roman navy. The Imperial War Museum has a collection of war paintings of particularly high quality. Many of them show the machinery and technology of war — guns, ships, planes, etc. — and many others show medical activity in the war zones. The National Army Museum also has many paintings of this kind on display, though mostly of less merit. So too does the Royal Air Force Museum, and the collection there also includes two fine sculptures inspired by the technology of flight: *Icarus* by Michael Ayrton and *Winged Figure* by Elizabeth Frink.

ART AND MILITARY SCIENCE

Art met combat and war in a different way up to the middle of the nineteenth century. The generals never ceased to call on the engineers and artificers for ever more efficient weapons and machines for slaughtering the enemy. But the engineers who made the weapons by hand and the purchasers who used them in ritualized fighting, in rehearsal, or in life-or-death combat, valued the craft that could add beauty to the objects through decoration and adornment. In the course of time, in a period stretching forward from the days

Opposite: Gassed *by John Singer Sargent 1917 (Imperial War Museum).*

Right: Bronze gun, probably Flemish, dated 1607, on a British carriage of 1827 (Royal Armories, Tower of London).

of the ancient Greeks, every part of every weapon and every plate of a suit of armour came to be seen as a surface that could be sculpted, engraved, inlaid, bejewelled, painted, or otherwise made pleasing to the eye.

London offers two great displays of personal armour and armament, at the Royal Armouries in the Tower of London and at the Wallace Collection. Here may be seen art put to the sword in the sense of decorating the blade, the hilt, the quillons, the pommel and the scabbard. And not only swords and daggers but also bills, halberds and poleaxes; and maces, clubs and hammers; and the corresponding products of the military engineers of the Near East and the Far East. In addition, there are displays of chain mail and plate armour with all parts of the body catered for, from sabatons for the feet to every variety of helmet for the head, and with covering also for most parts of the horse, except those where the animal was to be pricked by the rider's spurs. Smaller displays of arms and armour, but still of high quality, can be found at the Victoria and Albert Museum and at the National Army Museum.

The National Army Museum, Royal Armouries and Wallace Collection also have rich collections of firearms — matchlocks, flintlocks, blunderbusses and rifles as well as pistols. The gunsmiths' craft was used to bring together the barrel and stock, their engineering technology to create the gunlock, the firing mechanism, and then their aesthetic sense to decorate the various parts.

But the cannon is the weapon in which one can see the marriage of decorative art with military science on a grander scale. Although a cannon, like half a pair of trousers, is intrinsically restricted and limited in shape, the foundry technicians learned to add all manner of knobs, crests and curlicues to their moulds to give individuality and person-

ality to the guns they produced. The results can be seen along the pathways by the Royal Armouries in the Tower of London and in a far more impressive display at the Museum of Artillery where the cannon are up to 600 years old and the decoration develops from minimal to a bizarre mid-nineteenth-century ceremonial Burmese gun in the form of a dragon on a mahogany carriage.

THE BEST IN DESIGN

One can debate endlessly whether attractively designed but mass-manufactured products deserve to be counted as works of art. Certainly, some people respond to some motor cars as if they were — and if motor cars, why not kettles or computers?

Those who are prepared to accept that there is an aesthetic component in modern factory-made consumer products will be interested to see the display of household objects, the production of which has been engineered to accord with current artistic taste and which have been put on show (frequently changed) at the Design Museum. Items to be seen include not only ones such as those mentioned, but also kitchen implements, telephones, tables and chairs, clocks and radios, and many others — all of them the products of modern technology in manufacturing industry.

People hesitant to accord artistic status to present-day domestic objects will often, nevertheless, do so for similar articles of former times. Outstanding examples of beauty combined with precision engineering are to be found in the Clockmakers' Collection, which can be seen in Guildhall and in the horology galleries of the British Museum [BM Rooms 43-44]. Admittedly, what is meant by 'a beautiful pocket watch' or clock is a

Opposite: Eighteenth-century spy-glasses. Left, leather-covered with gilt decoration, silver bands and satinwood case behind (Italian); centre, five draw tubes and portraits of famous French authors round base (French); right, Wedgwood decoration of marriage of Cupid and Psyche (English) (British Optical Association Collection).

Right: Portrait of John Joseph Merlin by Thomas Gainsborough (The Iveagh Bequest, Kenwood).

beautiful case which encloses an exquisite but unseen movement. One is aware, however, of the latter, even if it is only the former that catches the eye. And when the objects are the beautifully decorated opera glasses, spectacle frames and cases, quizzing glasses, and similar devices, on view at the **British College of Optometrists**, both the art and the function are fully open to view.

In some products, you can see the mechanism of the object as well as the beauty and grace of the construction that embody it. At the **Iveagh Bequest, Kenwood**, in a chamber called Lord Mansfield's Dressing Room, there is a portrait by Gainsborough of John Joseph Merlin, an eighteenth-century inventor, and also some of the devices he designed. These include a 'skeleton' table clock, with all the inner wheels visible and the time showing on circular strips; a personal weighing machine, an early version of modern bathroom scales; and an invalid chair, called a 'gouty' chair, the movement of which is controlled by the seated patient.

SICKNESS AND ART
There seems to have been a strong link between sickness and artistic expression. On the walls of the Grand Staircase leading to the Great Hall of **St Bartholomew's Hospital** are two magnificent paintings by Hogarth. These are, respectively of *The Good Samaritan* and *The Healing of the Sick at the Pool of Bethesda*, by which Hogarth attempted to illustrate the spirit of the Hospital's work. Pictures of a similar kind are to be seen at the **Thomas Coram Foundation for Children** with works by Raphael and Gainsborough, as well as by Hogarth and others. These have a somewhat tenuous medical connection, even though the Foundation was from its origins concerned with the children's health as well as their welfare.

The Healing of the Sick at the Pool of Bethesda *(detail) by William Hogarth*
(St Bartholomew's Hospital).

An operating theatre is undoubtedly a place of drama, yet that drama has not often been conveyed to canvas. An exception is a rare painting by Barbara Hepworth at the **Royal College of Surgeons** of an operation in progress. A painting of similar theme and design, by Reginald Brill, hangs in the **Wellcome Library**. In these two pictures all the people on view are wearing surgical masks, caps and gowns. In two pictures hanging in the corridor of the Wellcome Trust opposite the library, *A tooth-drawer operating on a patient* (1620) by Rombouts, and *A surgeon operating for 'stone in the head'* (1569) by Huys, the characters are in everyday dress and it is not clear whether some of them are assistants or spectators.

Relatively enthusiastic pictures of medical people were produced by the portraitists who, of course, were commissioned for the purpose. **The Royal College of Physicians** has an outstanding collection of portraits, including paintings by Lawrence, Reynolds, Lely, Zoffany and others. The busts include one by Roubiliac of Dr Richard Meade. Two exceptional modern busts are one by Elizabeth Frink of Sir Raymond Hoffenberg, a recent President of the College, and one by Epstein of Lord Moran. There is a similar collection at the **Royal College of Surgeons**. The Surgeons' collection includes a magnificent painting by Holbein of *Henry VIII and the Barber Surgeons*; portraits of past presidents of the College by Kneller, Lawrence, Reynolds, and others; busts by Flaxman, Chantry, Nollekens and Roubiliac; and some fine animal paintings by Stubbs. There is also, in the entrance hall of the College, a remarkable double bust by Alfred Gilbert of Dr and Mrs MacLoghlin, which, moreover, contains their cremated ashes.

Of all the representations of medical people, however, one of the finest was falsely commissioned. It is a statue by Augustino Carlini in the **Victoria and Albert Museum**

[V&A Room 50A] of Joshua Ward. This was to have been set in Westminster Abbey, to acknowledge Ward's medical ability and philanthropy. Shortly before the ceremony, Ward was unmasked as having been a complete quack and Ward's Drops and Pills, out of which he had made his fortune, were recognized as useless.

Normally, the portrait painter was called in to commemorate the eminence of a particular physician or surgeon. An unusual instance of a patient portraying his doctor is to be seen in a portrait at the **Bethlem Royal Hospital Museum** by Richard Dadd, a nineteenth-century painter, who was confined as a patient in the hospital, an asylum for the insane founded in the thirteenth century. The collection at the museum contains a variety of interesting pictures, mostly by mentally disturbed people (among others, Nijinsky, the dancer, and Louis Wain, the illustrator, best known for his illustrations of cats) and two imposing statues, *Raving Madness* and *Melancholy Madness*, which originally stood over the gateway of an earlier site of the hospital in central London.

A tooth-drawer operating on a patient *by Theodoor Rombouts 1597-1637*
(The Wellcome Institute).

THE SPIRIT OF SCIENCE

Painters and sculptors have only rarely tried to capture the spirit of science or to show scientists, engineers or medical people in action. At the **National Gallery** [NG Room 39], there are two pretty pictures by Cornelius Troost — one of a doctor visiting a patient and the other showing a midwife and maid at the bedside of a woman in labour. But these are overshadowed by the painting by Hogarth in the same room, *The Visit to the Quack Doctor*, from the *Marriage à la Mode* series. Another painting of a doctor's visit, *The Sick Room* by Emma Brownlow, can be seen at the **Thomas Coram Foundation**.

At the **Royal Institution** there are three pictures showing famous scientists giving lecture-demonstrations. The oldest is a cartoon by Gillray, of a rollicking audience watching Humphrey Davy, in the year 1801, assisting in a demonstration of the effects of nitrous oxide (laughing gas). In a painting from the other end of the nineteenth century,

James Dewar explains to a distinguished audience the virtues of his vacuum flask. And in a painting of 1978 by Terence Cuneo, Lawrence Bragg is involved in an optical experiment in front of an audience of children at the annual Christmas Lectures. There is also, in the basement of the building, a watercolour by a Victorian amateur of Faraday's laboratory as it was when he worked in it, which guided its recent reconstruction. Apart from these pictures, the Royal Institution's collection includes many paintings and photographs of the eminent scholars who have worked there.

It remains the case, nevertheless, that although painters have frequently depicted artists, actors, musicians, farmers, soldiers and sailors, even jockeys and maidservants, at work, they have rarely done the same for engineers, scientists or medical practitioners. Even the products or the work-places of this group — the magnificent bridges and dams, the giant telescopes and accelerators, the laboratories, operating theatres, astronomical observatories, and so on — which members of the public invariably view with great awe and appreciation, have only rarely appeared on çanvas.

Ships at sea are a curious exception and there are occasional paintings of railway trains. One other exception is Stonehenge, the neolithic astronomical observatory. Just on these few subjects, many pictures can be seen in the London galleries. Particularly glorious examples are two paintings by Turner at the National Gallery [NG Room 35]: *The Fighting Téméraire* (of ships) and *Rain, Steam and Speed* (of a railway engine).

While painters have so rarely turned towards science, sculptors have in recent years occasionally tried to capture the spirit of the scientific age. An outstanding work in this category is Jacob Epstein's *Rock Drill* (1913) at the Tate Gallery [Tate Room 14, not always displayed], a figure combining menace, mechanical power, and servitude to man's instruction. In a different mood, *Meridian*, by Barbara Hepworth, outside State House, High Holborn, has an abstract quality, reflecting the arbitrary geometry of longitudes and latitudes, similarly caught by Wendy Taylor's *Timepiece*, in the garden of the Tower Hotel, St Katherine's Way. Another interesting work, which tries to capture something of the feeling of modern science and its associated technology, is *The Spirit of Electricity* by Geoffrey Clarke, sited on the north wall (in Litchfield Street) of the building at 4 St Martin's Street, formerly the head offices of Thorn-EMI plc.

In the restricted depiction of science, engineering and medicine, and their practitioners, to be found in London, the city is no different from others, in Great Britain and abroad. Generally, artists have been afraid of, or actively hostile towards, the sciences. This was explicitly the case for William Blake, who inveighed against the aridity (as he believed) of science, but nevertheless produced a wonderfully imaginative picture of *Newton*. As a woodcut, this image is sometimes put on view at the Tate Gallery as well as in the British Museum Print Room. The picture has recently been realized as a statue by Eduardo Paolozzi and is shortly to be erected in the entrance to the new British Library building.

Above: Rock Drill *by Jacob Epstein 1913 (Tate Gallery).*

Opposite: Rain, Steam and Speed *by J. M. W. Turner, 1844 (National Gallery).*

CHAPTER 5
MEMORIALS TO THE PRACTITIONERS
Remembrances of Scientists, Engineers, Physicians and Surgeons

The John Baird pub, Muswell Hill.

The nation has long respected and honoured scientists of outstanding importance. Newton and Darwin, for example, are both buried in Westminster Abbey. A couple of dozen other scientists, engineers and medical men also have graves there and as many again are remembered by inscriptions, busts or windows. A much smaller number have statues in public places in London — many more statues are erected to the field marshals and admirals who bring death and destruction to the enemy than to the doctors who cure the sick, or to the engineers who create the wealth of society.

STREETS, SCHOOLS AND BUILDINGS

Scientists, engineers and doctors, and sometimes their achievements, are remembered too in other ways. Streets, schools and

Opposite: Westminster Abbey.

Right: Statue of Robert Stephenson by Baron Carlo Marochetti (Euston Station).

buildings may be named after them. The dust settling on local council minutes has obscured which of the thirty-seven Nightingale Avenues, Roads, Streets, Walks and Ways were named after the medical reformer and which after the birds which once sang in the fields where the streets now run, but some are undoubtedly in memory of Florence Nightingale. Similarly, of the twenty-one named Newton, some were named after Isaac Newton and some after families of the same surname.

Certainly, however, all eight Brunel thoroughfares were named after one or other of the father and son engineers. Rennie Street (Southwark) is named after either John or George Rennie, another distinguished father-and-son pair of engineers. Flamsteed Road (Greenwich), Halley Road (Newham), and Halley Street (Tower Hamlets) are named after the astronomers. Occasionally local history can reveal a scientific connection. Howards Road (Newham) is named after Luke Howard (1772-1864), called the father of British meteorology, who introduced the universally-used names of cloud types and lived for a time in that road. Sloane Square, Sloane Avenue, Sloane Court, etc., in Chelsea are all named after Hans Sloane, lord of the manor containing the ground on which they were built. Similarly, Tradescant Road in Lambeth is named after John Tradescant (father and son were both John), the famous seventeenth-century horticulturists who had their gardens and nursery on land surrounding this road and who are immortalized by the names of the *Tradescantia* species of plants.

Michael Faraday has a school named after him in Southwark, as does Lister in Newham, Newton in Wandsworth, and Elizabeth Garrett Anderson in Islington. There is a pub named after John Baird (in Muswell Hill), the pioneer of television technology; Sir Alexander Fleming (in Paddington), the discoverer of penicillin; Daniel Gooch (in Bayswater), the railway engineer; Florence Nightingale (in Lambeth); and John Snow (in Soho), the 'father of epidemiology', who checked an outbreak of cholera in 1853 by taking the handle off the Broad Street pump, so forcing the local people to search for pure water.

PORTRAITS

Banknotes, in recent years, have carried portraits of Newton, Stephenson, Florence Nightingale, and Faraday. All the postage stamps that have ever been used in the UK can be seen at the National Postal Museum (see p.69). These have carried portraits of, among others, Newton, Darwin, Florence Nightingale, Lister, and Herschel, and pictures of Halley's comet, Fleming's culture of the *Penicillium* mould, ships, bridges, railway engines, and chemical structures, among many other items of scientific interest.

Left: Plaque in Upper Berkeley Street, marking the former home of Elizabeth Garrett Anderson, the first woman to qualify as a doctor in England.

Right: The tomb of Sir Hans Sloane at Chelsea Old Church.

A large number of scientists are remembered in the professional seclusion of the learned societies of which they were members. Nearly every society of this kind carries on its walls the portraits of former presidents and other high officers. In recently-founded societies these portraits are mostly photographs, but the older societies have often kept up the practice of remembering past presidents by commissioning an oil portrait. And the universities, research laboratories and institutes, local societies, and various other clubs and centres all tend to do the same, although usually in an unsystematic way.

WOMEN IN SCIENCE

Since no place was made for women in science or engineering until recent years, there are very few memorials to women in these professions. Streets and the pub named after Florence Nightingale (1820-1910) have already been mentioned; there is a plaque mark-ing the house in which she lived (10 South Street, W1), a Florence Nightingale Museum (see p.35), and a (private) hospital named after her (the Charter Nightingale Hospital).

As well as the school previously mentioned, Elizabeth Garrett Anderson (1836-1917) has a plaque on the house in which she lived (20 Upper Berkeley Street, W1), noting that she was the first woman to qualify as a doctor in Britain. She, too, has a hospital named after her.

There is a plaque marking the dwelling of Rosalind Franklin (1920-1958) (Donovan Court, Drayton Gardens, SW10), the crystallographer who played an important role in elucidating the structure of DNA. A similar plaque has been put up for the psychoanalyst Melanie Klein (1882-1960), (42 Clifton Hill, NW8).

CEMETERIES

All scientists die and, until recent years when cremation became the most common funeral practice, scientists filled their due proportion of space in the cemeteries. In earlier times, when there were few of them, London scientists were buried in London churchyards. As population pressures grew, the churchyards were filled. As a result, most graves of scientists from the late 1830s onwards are to be found in municipal rather than church cemeteries.

Of the great men of science who might have been buried with honour in the state pantheons, not all agreed to allow it. Fleming's ashes

are buried in St Paul's Cathedral and Rutherford's ashes are in Westminster Abbey. But Faraday, who held very strict religious views binding him to simplicity, insisted that he have a modest grave, which is to be found in the old cemetery at Highgate. Lister stated in his will that he should be buried alongside his wife and their joint grave is in Hampstead Cemetery.

There is no space here to list all the tombstones, plaques, busts, portraits and other memorials of all the significant scientists, engineers and doctors to be found in London. What follows is a short selection relating to some of the more significant characters.

BABBAGE, CHARLES (1791-1871), mathematician, FRS
Photograph: NPG, Room 16 (A. Claudet)
Residences (no plaques): 5 Devonshire Street, W1 and 1 Dorset Street, W1
Plaque: Larcom Street, SE17
Grave: Kensal Green Cemetery

Babbage is best remembered today in scientific circles for his construction of mechanical computers. His Difference Engines were limited to the standard arithmetic operations of addition, subtraction, multiplication and division; these were built and used for the calculation of logarithm tables and the like. His Analytic Engine would have had the capabilities, in principle, of a simple modern computer, but its construction was not completed. Displays dealing with the two machines can be seen in the Science Museum (2nd floor). Babbage was also a reformer in mid-Victorian society. He urged the collection of economic and social statistics and was a founder of what is now the Royal Statistical Society. He was a leader of the group who set about reforming the Royal Society in the 1850s. And he was also associated with the founding of the British Association for the Advancement of Science.

BACON, FRANCIS Lord Verulam (1st Viscount St Albans) (1561-1626), politician, civil servant and philosopher
Portrait: NPG, Room 2 (J. Vanderbank)
Statues: South Square, Gray's Inn; NPG, Room 2
Born: York House, Strand, of which only the remains of a river gate are left.

Bacon was one of the first modern philosophers of science. His books (*Advancement of Learning*, *New Atlantis*, *Novum Organum* and others) advocating the advantages of experimentation as the way forward for the sciences, inspired the founders of the Royal Society. He died from a chill caught while stuffing a fowl with snow in an attempt to study the effect of cold in delaying putrefaction. In his will he bequeathed funds to endow lectureships in science at Oxford and Cambridge. In the event, he died penniless and science lectureships were not established in those universities for another 250 years.

BANKS, SIR JOSEPH (1743-1820), botanist, FRS
Portraits: NPG, Room 11 (J. Reynolds): Roy Soc Council Chamber (T. Phillips)
Busts: Natl Maritime Musm (P. Turnerelli); British Museum
Plaque: 32 Soho Square, W1

Reynold's portrait of Banks (see p.148) shows him soon after his return from New Zealand and Australia, where he had sailed with Cook. Here he looks thoroughly confident and self-satisfied, as well he might, considering how much time he had spent in the bed of the Tahitian princess. He carried back to London a large collection of biological specimens — especially of plants. This brought him into royal favour and led to his unofficial directorship of the Royal Botanic Gardens, Kew, then private property of the King. The portrait by Phillips at the other end of his adult life shows him as the despotic head of British science, aggressive and conservative. He was President of the Royal Society for

Soho Square as it was at the time of Sir Joseph Banks, who lived in a house in the south-west corner.

42 years, from 1778 until his death, longer than anyone before or since. He vigorously opposed any changes in the organization of science in England. In particular, he opposed changing the Royal Society from its then status as a comfortable club for members of the nobility and gentlemen with interests in the sciences. His dead hand remained on the Society for another thirty years before the reformers were able eventually to reconstitute it as a professional body.

BRUNEL, ISAMBARD KINGDOM (1806-1859), civil engineer, FRS

Portrait: NPG (J. Horsley)

Statues: Victoria Embankment (corner of Temple Place) (C.Marochetti); Paddington Station (J. Doubleday)

Plaque: 98 Cheyne Walk, SW10

Tomb: Kensal Green Cemetery

Commemorative window: Westminster Abbey

Isambard Kingdom Brunel is more often remembered, perhaps because of his distinctive forenames, than his father, Sir Marc. But Sir Marc was also an engineer of the first rank. Father and son both lie in the family tomb and both names appear on the plaque of the house in which they lived in Chelsea. The father was the engineer of the world's first underwater tunnel, beneath the Thames at Rotherhithe. The son was appointed chief engineer of the project in 1827 and was nearly drowned the following year when water poured into the workings after a collapse of part of the structure. Isambard Brunel was appointed chief engineer to the Great Western Railway and in that capacity developed the railway lines, tunnels and bridges from London to the west of England. He also designed important ships: the *Great Western* (the first steamship for regular transatlantic travel), the *Great Britain* (the first ocean-going screw-driven steamer), and the *Great Eastern* (in 1858, the world's largest vessel ever built).

A plaque marking the former home of Henry Cavendish in Bedford Square.

CAVENDISH, HENRY (1731-1810), physicist FRS
Plaque: 11 Bedford Square, WC1

As a member of one of the richest families in England, of whom the Duke of Devonshire was the head, Henry Cavendish inherited a fortune. This allowed him to set up private laboratories in his country house in Clapham and in his town residence in Bedford Square, as well as filling another house in Dean Street, Soho, with his private library. He was a brilliant experimentalist and is particularly remembered in the history of science for making the first reliable measurement of Newton's constant of gravitation and for verifying Coulomb's inverse square law of electrical force. He was also a morbidly shy recluse and an extreme misogynist. There is only one known extant portrait of him. He is said to have ordered his meals by notes to his butler left outside his study door; to have tried to avoid any social contacts with women; and to have forbidden his female domestic servants ever to appear in his presence, on pain of instant dismissal.

DARWIN, CHARLES (1809-1892), naturalist, FRS
Portraits: NPG Room 16 (J. Collier), (many copies elsewhere); Down House
  (G. Richmond)
Statue: Natural History Museum
Plaques: Biological Sciences Building, University College, site of 110 Gower Street, WC1;
  and Down House (Darwin Museum) Downe, Orpington, Kent.
Tomb: Westminster Abbey

Darwin is one of the few people of whom it can be said that they changed the outlook of our civilization. What changed *his* outlook was his work as the naturalist on the five-year voyage (1831-1836) of the *Beagle* to the Galapagos Islands and the coast of South America. This led him to appreciate the way in which the varieties of animals appeared to radiate from ancestral patterns. After twenty years of amassing more evidence, he published in 1859 *The Origin of the Species by Means of Natural Selection*. He wrote several more books over the next twenty years, as well as bearing the vituperation of his Creationist vilifiers. The opponents died off, the supporters grew in number, and Darwin was eventually given national honour on his death by burial at Westminster Abbey.

Portrait of Charles Darwin in 1840 by George Richmond (Down House).

DAVY, HUMPHREY (1778-1823), chemist, FRS

Portraits: NPG Room 14 (T. Phillips); miniature, NPG Room 15 (J. Jackson);
   Roy Inst (anon); Roy Soc (T. Lawrence)
Commemorative tablet: Westminster Abbey

Son of a Cornish wood-carver and initially appreticed to an apothecary, Davy found employment in 1798 with a Bristol physician and there pursued his studies of the effects of nitrous oxide ('laughing gas'). There too he met and estáblished life-long friendships with the poets Coleridge, Southey and Wordsworth, and himself began writing poetry. At the age of 22, Davy moved to the Royal Institution where he later became professor of chemistry. At that time the chemist John Dalton wrote of him: 'He is a very amiable and intelligent young man and we have extremely interesting conversations of an evening. His principal defect — as a philosopher — is that he does not smoke.' In 1820 he was elected President of the Royal Society. His discoveries and isolation of several elements (see p.139), his work on agricultural chemistry, and his studies of coal mine explosions make Davy one of the greatest of British scientists. In 1812, as Director of the Royal Institution, he gave employment to Faraday as his assistant (see below). In 1813, because of his scientific eminence, Davy was given permission by the government in London and by Napoleon in Paris to visit and study the volcanoes of the Auvergne, even though Britain and France were at war. He travelled widely and died in Geneva.

FARADAY, MICHAEL (1791-1867), physicist and chemist, FRS

Portraits: NPG Room 16 (T. Phillips); Roy Inst
Statue: Roy Inst (J. Foley); copy outside Inst Elect Engrs
Plaques: 48 Blandford Street, W1 and Faraday House,
   Hampton Court Road
Grave: Highgate (West) Cemetery

The plaque in Blandford Street marks the house in which Faraday lived while apprenticed to a bookbinder (see p.200). In 1812 he was employed to assist Davy at the Royal Institution. Within a year, Sir Humphrey and Lady Davy took him on their tour of France and then on to Italy, Switzerland, and Germany, but treating him as their valet rather than as a scientific assistant. Gay-Lussac, impressed by Faraday's insight and scientific potential, protested to Davy at this treatment, but to no effect. Faraday also met, on the journey, Ampère, Volta and other leading scientists. In 1825 Faraday was appointed director of chemistry at the Royal Institution and then continued to accumulate the discoveries which rank him as one of the world's pre-eminent experimental scientists. These ranged over much of chemistry and physics. Of foremost consequence to the world was the generation of electricity by moving a magnet near a loop of wire, the dynamo effect. It is said that when asked, after a lecture explaining his discovery, of what use it was, he replied: 'Madam, of what use is a newborn baby ?'

Statue of Michael Faraday by J. Foley (Royal Institution).

FRANKLIN, BENJAMIN (1706-1790), statesman and scientist, FRS

Portraits: terracotta plaque, NPG Room 11 (J. B. Nini); wax relief miniature,
Wallace Collection, Room 2 (anon); Royal Society (J. Wright); British Optical
Association Collection
Effigy: Madame Tussaud's
Plaque: 36 Craven Street, WC2

Franklin, born in Boston, Massachusetts, was a British citizen at birth, but an American at death, having played a prominent part in the movement for independence of the U.S.A. He is, surprisingly, one of the most memorialized scientists in London. He is the only scientist to have an effigy in Madame Tussaud's Waxworks — save for Wren who is exhibited as an architect. There is a Benjamin Franklin Room in the RSA building (see p.123). At the British Optical Museum in the British College of Optometrists (see p.21) is a pair of the bifocal spectacles that he invented, alongside a sketch of him. The house in Craven Street (see p.185) is slowly being converted into a Benjamin Franklin Museum. Apart from his well-known studies of atmospheric electricity and lightning, he also examined the effect of oil in calming rough water.

Portrait of Benjamin Franklin by Joseph Wright of Derby (Royal Society).

FREUD, SIGMUND (1856-1939), psychoanalyst, For.Memb.RS

Portrait: Freud Museum (S. Dali)
Statue: Swiss Cottage Library Complex, Adelaide Road, NW3 (O. Nemon)
Plaques: 20 Maresfield Gardens, NW3 (Freud Museum); 2 Warrington Crescent, W9
(Collonade Hotel)

Freud came to London on 6 June 1938 to escape from Hitler's persecution of Jews, and died on 23 September 1939. A small plaque at Golders Green Crematorium records his cremation there. Knowledge of psychoanalysis and the fame of the founder of the movement preceded his arrival in England. Freud by then was dying of cancer and in considerable pain, yet was besieged by newspapers, admirers and detractors. He spent his first few months in London in rented accommodation further down Maresfield Gardens before moving into the house that bears the plaque and has become the Freud Museum. Between the two residences, he spent a couple of weeks in hospital and a couple of days (while the second house was being made ready) in the hotel that now records his stay with a plaque.

HUNTER, JOHN (1728-1793), anatomist and surgeon, FRS

Portraits: Roy Coll Surgeons (J. Reynolds) (many copies elsewhere) and another (R. Home)
Busts: Roy Coll Surgeons (J. Flaxman); Leicester Square
Plaque: 31 Golden Square, W1
Tomb: Westminster Abbey

Surgery was brought from a craft to a science by Hunter, who based his work on an unrivalled knowledge of anatomy and of physiological function. John Hunter did not complete a formal medical education, but gained his knowledge assisting at his brother William's anatomy school, spending some time as a pupil at St Bartholomew's Hospital and then practising as an army surgeon. He returned to London in 1763 and established his own school. The school grew in fame as Hunter amassed for teaching purposes a large anatomical and pathological collection. After he died, this collection became the core of the Hunterian Museum of the Royal College of Surgeons. From 1768 he was surgeon to St George's Hospital and from 1776 surgeon-extraordinary to George III. He was one of the leaders of his profession. Many of the greatest surgeons of the nineteenth century were his pupils; and among his patients were Byron, Haydn, Gainsborough, Hume, Reynolds and Adam Smith.

Portrait of John Hunter, copied (in enamel on copper) by Henry Bone from the original by Sir Joshua Reynolds (Royal College of Surgeons).

JENNER, EDWARD (1749-1823), medical practitioner, FRS

Portraits: NPG Room 14 (J. Northcote); Roy Coll Physicians (T. Lawrence)
Statue: Kensington Gardens (W. Calder Marshall)

After an apprenticeship to a surgeon in the west of England, Jenner came to London in his twenties to study with John Hunter. He also, at the invitation of Sir Joseph Banks, arranged and catalogued the collection of plant specimens brought back by Banks and Captain Cook from their voyage to the south Pacific and Australasia. On completing his training, he returned to the west country and developed the technique of vaccination, inoculating a subject with the material from a patient suffering from cow-pox as a preventative against smallpox. Despite the evidence he presented, there was initial scepticism of Jenner's procedure until members of the royal family took an interest in it and leading surgeons and physicians began to advocate it. Then Jenner was flooded with applications for treatment and claimed he had become 'the vaccine clerk of the whole world.' In recognition of his work, he was voted £10,000 by Parliament in 1802 and then a further £20,000 in 1806.

LISTER, JOSEPH (1827-1912), surgeon, FRS

Portrait: Roy Coll Surgeons (J. Ouless)
Busts: Portland Place (T. Brock); NPG Room 16 (T. Brock)
Portrait medallions: Westminster Abbey (T. Brock); University College London
Plaque: 12 Park Crescent, W1
Grave: Hampstead Cemetery

Lister came from a Quaker family, his father a wine merchant, amateur scientist and Fellow of the Royal Society. Lister enrolled as a medical student at University College, London, qualified in 1850, and was appointed to a lectureship in surgery at Edinburgh. There he proved himself a first-class surgeon and also began a productive research career, as well as marrying the daughter of the professor of surgery. In 1860 he, too, was elected an FRS, in recognition of his studies on inflammation. In the same year he was appointed Regius Professor of Surgery at Glasgow. Five years later he discovered the antiseptic properties of carbolic acid, thereby introducing asepsis into surgical practice. Lister also introduced catgut, which could eventually be absorbed by the body, for making surgical ligatures, in place of the then general use of silk or hemp, which could not be absorbed. He moved to the chair of surgery at Edinburgh in 1867 and then, in 1877, to the chair at King's College, London, where he remained until he retired in 1903. The fall in

Portrait medallion commemorating Joseph Lister (University College London).

mortality from surgery was so great as a result of the introduction of Lister's methods that he was regarded with veneration and received awards from many countries. He was knighted in 1883, raised to the peerage in 1897 (the first medical man so honoured), awarded the Order of Merit and appointed a Privy Counsellor. He served as President both of the Royal College of Surgeons and of the Royal Society.

MAXWELL, JAMES CLERK (1831-1879), physicist, FRS

Plaque: 16 Palace Gardens Terrace, W8
Memorial inscription: Westminster Abbey

Maxwell was born in Edinburgh and studied at the universities of Edinburgh and Cambridge. He was a brilliant mathematician and theoretical physicist and began his output of discovery with a paper published in the *Proceedings* of the Royal Society of Edinburgh while he was still a schoolboy. To some extent Maxwell remained a schoolboy through his relatively short life, enjoying a Victorian sense of humour and being devoted, until near his death, to playing with the toy called a diabolo, which all his friends associated with him. But at the same time, he was able to make fundamental contributions to physics. His most productive years were 1860-1865 when he was professor of physics at King's College, London. He applied himself at that time to the theory of colour vision, the study of gases, thermodynamics, and above all to electromagnetic theory. In this last subject, Maxwell was able to take the ideas about electric and magnetic forces, expressed intuitively by Faraday, and clothe them in precise mathematical terms. His results led within a few years to the discovery of radio waves by Hertz in Germany. Maxwell's theory was a fundamental basis, in turn, for the work done a few decades later by Einstein.

NEWTON, ISAAC (1642-1727), mathematician and physicist, FRS

Portraits: NPG Room 4 (G. Kneller); Roy Soc (J. Vanderbank)
Busts: Tate Room 4 (E. Hodges, after Roubiliac); Leicester Square
Plaques: 87 Jermyn Street, SW1; (on site now occupied by Westminster Public Library); St Martin's Street, WC2
Tomb: Westminster Abbey

The bust of Sir Isaac Newton in Leicester Square.

The story of Newton and the apple is well known and the incident occurred, if indeed it happened, while Newton had returned from Cambridge to his mother's house at the time of the plague in 1665. Nearly all of Newton's great scientific work was done while he was officially in residence at the university. In London he was a man of affairs. The graduates of the University of Cambridge elected Newton as their Member of Parliament where he served from 1689 to

1690 and again from 1701 to 1705. In 1699 Newton was appointed Master of the Mint. At this juncture he resigned his university professorship and did little scientific research thereafter. However, he continued to engage in scientific controversy, especially in acrimonious defence of his own ideas. From 1703 until his death, Newton was President of the Royal Society and played an active role in the Society's administration. Manuscripts left by him show that he made a great effort, at that time, on what seem to have been cabbalistic studies, the purpose and conclusions of which have still not been fully deciphered.

RUTHERFORD, ERNEST (1871-1937), physicist, FRS

Portraits: NPG Room 27 (J. Dunn); Roy Soc (O. Birley)
Tomb: Westminster Abbey

The instinctive understanding of the physical world shown by Faraday was shared by Rutherford who also, however, had the mathematical ability that Faraday lacked. It was Rutherford who first disentangled the phenomena of radioactivity. He was the first to set up the model of the atom comparable to the solar system, with a central small nucleus circled by electrons. And it was he who first achieved in the laboratory the transmutation of elements, of which alchemists had dreamed some 500 years earlier. He came to England from New Zealand and worked successively in Cambridge, Montreal, Manchester and then again Cambridge. He once said that there were only two kinds of science — physics and stamp collecting; he meant that scientists can study and explain fundamental particles and forces (as he did), or else merely assemble facts. However, the Nobel prize he won was for chemistry. He became Lord Rutherford, was awarded the Order of Merit and was made President of the Royal Society.

SLOANE, HANS (1660-1753), physician and naturalist, FRS

Portraits: NPG Room 6 (S. Slaughter); Roy Coll Physicans
Statue: British Museum (J. M. Rysbrack) (copy in Chelsea Physic Garden)
Plaques: 4 Bloomsbury Place, WC1; Kings Mead, King's Road, SW3
Bust: British Museum (J. M. Rysbrack)
Grave: Churchyard, Chelsea Old Church

At the age of nineteen, Sloane came to London to study medicine under the tutelage of the Society of Apothecaries. In using the herbal garden that the society had established on leased ground in Chelsea, he became interested in botany and his studies at the universities of Paris and Montpellier confirmed this interest. While in Jamaica (1687-1689), as private physician to the Duke of Albemarle, Sloane classified about 800 plant species and brought many specimens back to England. On his return to England, he practised as a physician and became one of the most fashionable in London. Visitors to his house in Bloomsbury Square included Handel, Voltaire and Linneaus. Sloane helped the Society of Apothecaries to extend the Chelsea Physic Garden, the freehold of which he presented to that Society. Sloane was President of the Royal College of Physicians 1719-1735 and President of the Royal Society 1727-1741 — the only person to hold the two posts simultaneously. His great collection of books and curiosities was bequeathed to the nation (on condition that his family received £20,000) and became the nucleus of the British Museum. His portrait appears on the inn sign of the Museum Tavern in Great Russell Street, opposite the British Museum.

STEPHENSON, ROBERT (1803-1859), railway engineer, FRS

Portrait: NPG Room 16 (J. Lucas)
Statue: Euston Station forecourt (C. Marochetti)
Plaque: 35 Gloucester Square, W2
Grave and commemorative window: Westminster Abbey

The Westminster Abbey window, in the North Aisle of the choir, commemorates Robert Stephenson together with his father George. To the father goes the honour of engineering the first steam-powered railway, from Stockton to Darlington, in 1825, but Robert assisted in preliminary surveying of the line. Robert also assisted his father for some years in the construction of locomotives, including the *Rocket* which, in 1829, won the famous Rainhill speed trials and then ran on the new line between Liverpool and Manchester. Robert Stephenson was responsible for the engineering of many railways in Great Britain and abroad. He was also the engineer of many important bridges, especially tubular bridges at Conway, Berwick and Newcastle, across the St Lawrence at Montreal and across the Nile at Damietta. He was a Member of Parliament in the years 1847-1859.

The Museum Tavern in Great Russell Street, opposite the British Museum, with a portrait of Sir Hans Sloane on the inn sign.

CHAPTER 6
SHOPPING FOR SCIENCE
Instruments, Books, Antiques, and Children's Science

I f you wished to set up an amateur's laboratory in a room at home from items bought over the counter in London, how far could you get? Without difficulty you could find computers and cameras and those items of electronic communication which have recently become classed as domestic goods. In some toyshops you could buy kits for children to set up a proto-laboratory in the nursery. In some specialized shops selling antiques and at auctions you might buy the instruments used in their laboratories by scientists in the nineteenth century. But what if you yourself want to engage in science at home? There would not be too much difficulty in finding books to tell you what items of apparatus you need, but could you locate the shops that sell them?

COMPUTER TECHNOLOGY AND ELECTRONIC COMMUNICATIONS
In just about every district of London, it is now possible to buy a computer with a monitor screen and printer, and a modem allowing the computer to transmit or receive information down telephone lines. This makes it possible — in principle and if you have obtained an identification code — for you to access all the great data banks of the world. In turn, this gives you the power of calling up information on a scale undreamed of twenty-five years ago. The chain from user to computer to telephone line to data bank puts the amateur on a par with the professional.

Furthermore, the desk-top computers you can buy in the high streets of London have an analytic power and calculating capability superior to that of the biggest computers of twenty-five years ago. As a result, many problems in computational mathematics and even in logic could be studied by the home-based amateur. Thus work using only a computer might be started bv a determined Londoner within only an hour or so of setting out from home.

Opposite: Arthur Middleton's antique scientific instrument shop in New Row.

Right: Wallace Heaton's photographic shop in New Bond Street.

The citizens' band allows anyone to operate a radio transmitter, though only over a very limited frequency range, and these are readily available in local shops. In principle, you might make a scientific study of radio wave behaviour in this frequency band, but it is well-trodden territory and not of much interest. More elaborate investigations would need more elaborate equipment. The starting point is simple: a power source, provided by batteries or the electric mains, plenty of wire, and a few tools; and all of these are universally available.

The next step up is probably a signal detector and perhaps a signal generator and an oscilloscope. We have learned recently that with these items you could listen in to private telephone conversations between well-known people, but that's collecting gossip, not scientific information. For the latter, you would need to exercise some know-how and rig up aerials to allow detection of atmospheric electric effects or of radio waves from distant stars and galaxies, as an adventure in radio astronomy. An occasional high-quality suburban electronics shop might sell the necessary equipment. If you cannot find such a shop locally, you will need to go to Tottenham Court Road or Edgware Road, where several shops specialize in such equipment. At the specialist shops, too, you could buy electronic components of all sorts as well as meters for various electric measurements. The transistor and integrated circuit devices that these shops also sell, but which can sometimes be bought from a local radio repairer, allow you to build your own instruments at a fraction of shop prices.

OPTICAL EQUIPMENT

In most of London's shopping centres, you can buy very high-quality photographic cameras, binoculars and telephoto lenses, which were the total equipment of amateur naturalists a few decades ago. If your local shop does not sell them, you will certainly be able to find them in ones like Wallace Heaton or Jessop in central London. Also to be bought in any high street are video-cameras (camcorders) which, although meant to provide pictures for display on a television screen, can be fed to a desk-top computer equipped with a frame-grabbing card (ordered through the local computer shop). Such a card dumps a picture into the computer's store. Then you are set up for picture documenting, image processing or pattern recognition research.

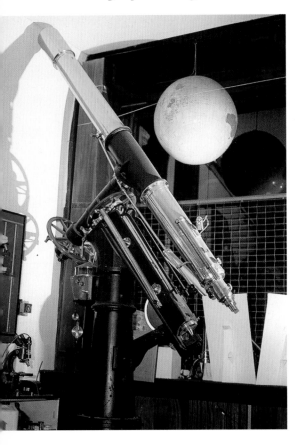

If, rather than looking at birds and animals, you want to look at very distant objects, the stars and galaxies, you need a telescope. Some local photographers sell small telescopes, typically with lenses up to about 5 cm in diameter, occasionally larger, but rarely of good quality. Intending London astronomers are lucky in having a splendid telescope shop available, Broadhurst, Clarkson & Fuller in Farringdon Road. This is one of the last true science shops in London, other than the shops attached to some of the museums. Here you can buy any size of telescope from a 3 cm refractor up to a 60 cm reflector. You could walk out with your purchase if you wished, although you would need a good-sized truck to carry the large reflector! Here, too, you can buy a wide range of astronomers' accessories — equatorials, telescope mountings, lenses, mirrors, chronometers, etc., as well as star maps, celestial globes and a wide range of astronomy books.

Should your interest be in very small objects and creatures, rather than the very

Above: Antique telescope at Broadhurst, Clarkson & Fuller.

Right: The shopfront of Broadhurst, Clarkson & Fuller, the telescope shop in Farringdon Road.

large and distant galaxies, you need a microscope. Among the advertisers in the first issue of *Nature,* published in 1869, are six suppliers, all situated in central London, who offered quality microscopes for sale. Today, apart from Broadhurst, Clarkson & Fuller, there are just two shops — John Bell & Croyden and Porter Nash, both in Wigmore Street — where you could purchase a good-quality instrument. There are several suppliers — photographers and others — offering inexpensive but low-quality microscopes, where 'inexpensive' means a price between about £25 for a child's microscope and seven or eight times as much for the minimum that would be acceptable to a serious amateur. If you wish to buy a research-quality instrument (which now costs several thousand pounds), the order will need to be sent by post.

MEDICAL INSTRUMENTS

Of the scientific professions, it seems that only the medical people are well served by retail suppliers. You can buy over the counter the instruments to set up a GP's consulting room, an operating theatre, or many kinds of specialized clinic.

Downs in New Cavendish Street specializes in hand-held surgical instruments and electro-surgical items. The company's catalogue lists 27,000 lines, although only items normally called for are kept in stock. Also in New Cavendish Street, Daniels carries about 5,000 items in stock, covering surgical and diagnostic instruments, dressings, and hospital furnishings. Seward's, a few steps along the same street and also in Great Suffolk Street, offers a similar range of products. In Wigmore Street, mention has already been made of John Bell & Croyden and Porter Nash, as sellers of microscopes; both also sell a very wide range of medical and surgical equipment and pharmaceuticals.

CHEMISTRY

The laboratory suppliers for chemistry have, for the most part, moved out of London and work almost exclusively by mail order. Again the shops to go to are the pharmacists, John Bell & Croyden and Porter Nash. These two retailers, together with Bernard Muller in Fulham, are probably the last remaining shops to which you can still go and buy a test tube, a retort stand, a Bunsen burner, or a length of rubber tubing. And even if you have a supply of flasks and pipettes and condensers, it is not easy to find the chemical reagents. John Bell & Croyden maintains a good stock, but the local pharmacists who were once stockists of many common chemical substances now tend to buy in their medicaments in made-up form, so no longer keep the materials on which they formerly relied.

You must remember that many of the substances — benzene and mercury are examples — that were once in unrestricted use in school and university chemistry laboratories, have in recent years been declared hazardous or toxic or both. Their supply is therefore now subject to control.

The knowledgeable person, however, could still get some way to building up a chemical store by purchases in the local shops. Copper and ammonium salts, baking powder (mostly sodium bicarbonate), caustic soda (sodium hydroxide), methylated spirit (methanol), spirit of salts (hydrochloric acid) and several other substances of use in a chemical laboratory are sold by ordinary domestic suppliers.

Unfortunately, however, the reagents in this stock would all be at a low level of purity. In this situation, it might be better, if you wish to go in for chemistry, to start with what is on offer in children's toy stores.

SCIENCE BOOKS

If you go into an average London bookshop to buy science books, how deep into science will they take you? The answer, in the average shop, is not very far. In the section on science for adults, there are always books of popular science which provide superficial surveys of limited but fashionable topics. These for a decade or more have included ecology, genetic engineering, the 'big bang' theory of the origin of the universe, and the social impact of computers. There may also be a few useful paperback dictionaries of some branches of science, but little straightforward exposition of the fundamentals of the basic science and engineering subjects.

The lack of depth in the populist approach to science for adults, and the curious unevenness of bookstore coverage, can be seen in several instances. For example, there are usually many books on sale dealing with health to the extent of recommending diets, exercise schedules, relaxation programmes, and the like. Yet it is rare to find even an elementary book on how the body actually works — that is, on human physiology. Similarly, there may be books (probably in the hobbies or leisure sections) detailing how to strip down and re-assemble a motor car, yet nothing on the engineering principles of torques and thrusts, or in explanation of friction and wear of tyres or of the engineering arguments for front or rear mounted engines.

In the suburban and typical central London bookshops, there is often a selection of books on computers available. Some of these give the rudiments of how computers work. It is usually possible, too, to find detailed instruction books on the more popular word processing and data base systems, though less easy to find books on programming. For such books you must go either to the specialized computer shops found in most suburbs or to the central London specialist computer shops, to be found in the areas of Tottenham Court Road, Edgware Road, and in some parts of the City.

General selections of scientific textbooks and advanced specialist books (in subjects including the many branches of medicine and engineering) can be found in only a few bookshops in central London. Particularly recommended are central London branches of Dillon's (including its Science Museum branch) and Waterstone's, Foyle's in Charing Cross Road, and the Modern Book Co in Praed Street. The two shops at the Natural History Museum offer a fair range of books on biology, natural history topics, and earth sciences. Exclusively for medical books, the BMJ Bookshop in Burton Street provides an excellent selection. Most universities and colleges have a bookshop either on campus or nearby; however the London ones, except for those central bookshops just listed, tend to carry only the recommended course books of the institution in question. Dillon's in Torrington Place and Foyle's also stock school textbooks.

There are several monthly magazines devoted to photography, computing, and electronics, aimed at the keen amateur. These are carried by most newsagents, who also usually sell the *New Scientist*, the world's leading popular science weekly. If you want to buy *Scientific American*, the excellent monthly of popular science, you may need to hunt for a superior newsagent, but can probably find one locally. However, if you wish to buy one of the professional weeklies, such as *Nature* or the *British Medical Journal* which are normally despatched only to subscribers, Dillon's in Torrington Place seems to be one of the very few shops that takes a few copies for casual sale.

Opposite: The bookshop at the Natural History Museum.

Right: The shop of John Bell & Croyden, pharmacists and suppliers of medical instruments, chemical apparatus, reagents, etc.

Illustration from the book Concordantia Astronomiae cum Theologia *by Petrus de Alliaco. auctioned at Sotheby's in December 1993.*

ANTIQUARIAN BOOKS

Science advances so rapidly that most research monographs need new editions within not more than five years. Textbooks, if they are to survive, are usually rewritten after a decade or less. Old books which pass down from one student to another typically fall to pieces after one or two such passages. Those in the collection of a professional worker are usually found to be unsellable after the person's death and end up in the rubbish dump. However, books that have survived a century or more acquire both historical and antiquarian status and as such are collected by librarians and bibliophiles respectively.

It is not possible to list the many distinguished antiquarian booksellers of London. Two, however, specialize in books of science and medicine. These are R. Connelly at the Vade Mecum Press in Great Ormond Street, and Rogers Turner Books of Nelson Road, Greenwich. Other sources of antiquarian scientific books are the auction rooms. The most reliable of these are the great auction houses in the centre of town, Christie's, Sotheby's, Phillips and Bonham's.

ANTIQUE SCIENTIFIC INSTRUMENTS

London is the world centre of the international trade in antiquarian scientific instruments. Like old scientific books, old scientific instruments are hunted by museum curators and collectors, although in most cases antiquity descends on instruments after fifty years, or even less, rather than after a hundred. The antique instruments are placed in museums to illustrate the history of science; but collectors acquire them mostly for decorative value.

Clocks and barometers are exceptions: they are usually used for what they are. And an exception is sometimes made for ancient microscopes, which occasionally are put to use. It is difficult, however, to imagine a sensible modern use for a Wimshurst Machine or a gold leaf electroscope.

The same auction houses as listed above for books — Christie's, Sotheby's, Phillips and Bonham's — hold two or three sales a year of antique scientific instruments, some of which fetch prices in the range of tens of thousands of pounds. The leading dealer in these objects is Trevor Philip & Son in Jermyn Street, Piccadilly;

Above: Rare table globe by Thomas Malby & Son, dated 1868, demonstrating the movement of the Sun with respect to the Earth, sold by Trevor Philip & Sons.

Right: The shop of Trevor Philip & Sons, dealers in antique scientific instruments, in Jermyn Street.

others with shops open in normal trading hours include D. Howard and D. & E. Squires in King's Road, Chelsea, and A. Middleton in New Row, Covent Garden. There are also some who operate in the Portobello Road market on Saturdays, including P. Delehar and S. Talbot.

CHILDREN'S SCIENCE

The keen curiosity of children of all ages in the world about them is well served by sets, kits, and toys now on the market. Some of these have been developed for children as young as five. Children aged ten and above are far better served in the provision of scientific equipment than are amateur adults. There are many toyshops in London, and also the museum shops at the Science Museum, the Natural History Museum, and one or two oth-

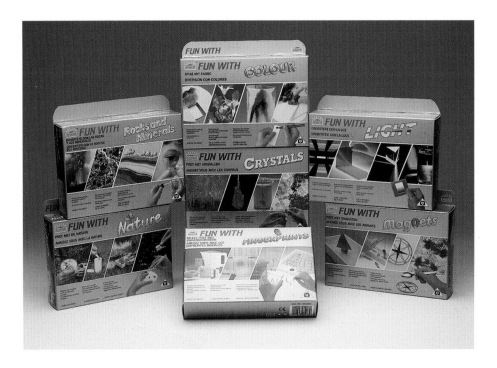

Science kits for young children, marketed by Peter Pan Playthings.

ers, which sell starter sets for various scientific studies. The most elaborate sets in the major toyshops, especially Hamley's of Regent Street, Harrod's in Knightsbridge, and Selfridges in Oxford Street, are sometimes, indeed, bought by adults for their own use.

The most impressive sets are those aimed at the young intending microscopist. Those at the expensive end of the range provide (for between £50 and £100) a monocular microscope with up to a ✗1200 magnification (although a narrow field of view), an internal light source, a built-in photomicrography system, a preparation kit, and a useful instruction book. In the same price range you could buy a young astronomer a refractor telescope with a 50 mm lens.

Traditionally, the young scientist at home sets about creating a chemistry lab in a cellar or attic room with a water supply. The chemistry kits on sale in toy shops come in a range of sizes (priced in the range £10-£75) and the biggest state that, although aimed at children of 10 or more, there should always be adult supervision while the child is following through the experiments described in the instruction booklets.

Nevertheless, the largest of the chemistry sets contains samples of only about two dozen chemical reagents. Few if any of these are outside the range of substances which, as suggested above, can be bought in local stores. There is the advantage, however, that the samples in the chemistry sets are of sufficient purity for the experiments listed in the instruction booklets to work correctly.

The young would-be biologist is less well provided for. Biology is mostly a study of the natural world and no biology starter set for children could contain living animals. The sets specializing in botany do usually contain packets of seeds and perhaps also some compost mixture. The zoological sets typically provide insect traps and a magnifying glass for looking at the creatures caught. Also, in this area, there are some good construction kits for making model skeletons, bodies, or various body organs. For all the biological kits, the accompanying booklets of instructions and suggestions are able to open the subject out rather more widely than is managed in the corresponding books for other subjects.

With physical science and engineering, the kits return to a higher degree of complexity. With compendiums of various sizes (in a price range similar to that of chemistry kits) the experimenter can explore some of the properties of light, electricity, magnetism, engine mechanisms, and some other processes. Several toys on the market offer a beginning in electronic engineering with the construction of simple systems — crystal radios, Morse code telegraphs, and the like. And others do the same for mechanical engineering.

It would be unfair not to mention, also, some of the seemingly low-level starter sets, which could fire a child's imagination just as effectively as the most expensive and elaborate chemistry or microscopy set. One such, aimed at mineralogy, contains fifteen or so rock specimens, a gram or two of each, stuck to a card, together with a magnifying glass for examining them more closely, and a booklet of simple explanation. The child who responds to this introduction could almost certainly find samples of granites, sandstones, limestones, etc., in abundance anywhere in London, as building materials or in garden stones, and thus begin on a path of discovery of which the end is in the stars.

Also to be specially mentioned are simple science-based toys: things for giving fun and pleasure, rather than instruction. The museum shops, particularly those at the Science Museum and the Natural History Museum, are good sources for them.

As with the provision of scientific equipment, children tend to be better served than adults in the books written for them. In the children's section of the typical bookshops there are usually several good introductions, at the appropriate level for the age indicated, to the main branches of science. However, in such shops there are very rarely school textbooks for sale: it is assumed that these will be provided by the schools.

IN OUR DAILY LIVES
This survey of the range of objects directly related to science that can be bought over-the-counter in London has omitted some of the most remarkable applications of science in our daily lives. Obviously, you can buy radios and television sets, motor cars, microwave ovens and a host of other things which incorporate the most advanced technology. We suppose that you would not buy such objects in order to try some scientific experiments. But you could: there is in fact a vast number of experiments and studies you could undertake with these items.

The same is true for items that cost much less or even cost nothing. You can always just observe the behaviour of the animals and plants in your garden or in the park. A cheap and small hand lens may be of help in looking at small insects, or parts of the plant structure; and a book from the public library may help give you a sense of direction.

The fact is that the possibilities of scientific study are all around you in London.

CHAPTER 7
JOURNEYING WITH THE SCIENCES
Four Walks and an Excursion

The walks given here are offered as examples of a possible way of exploring London and noting the intimate connection of science, medicine, and engineering with its streets, buildings and history. London is too vast for a few such journeys to cover more than a minute fraction of the explorations that can be made. Other districts that would yield as rich an interest include Chelsea, Bloomsbury, Bayswater and Paddington, Southwark, and Islington, to name only the most obvious. Help for such excursions can be had from local guidebooks and lists of commemorative plaques, which are usually carried by good local bookshops. The bookshop at Guildhall Library has a particularly good selection of such books.

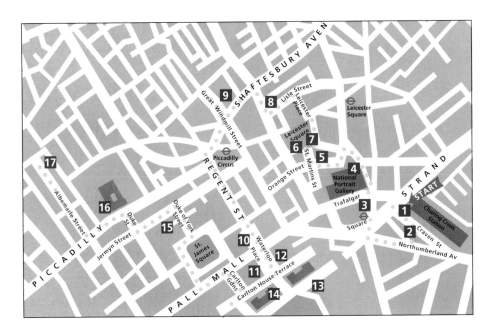

WALK NO.1
TRAFALGAR SQUARE, PALL MALL AND PICCADILLY AREA

This walk will probably take between two and three hours, but if you have extra time available you may like to spend it at the National Portrait Gallery (NPG, [4] in the itinerary), meeting the scientists, engineers, physicians and surgeons whose likenesses are to be seen there.

START in the courtyard of Charing Cross Station. Turn left into the Strand, under the arcade fronting no.11, and immediately left again into Craven Street. BENJAMIN FRANKLIN lived for most of the time between 1757 and 1775 at 36 Craven Street [1], now called Benjamin Franklin House and being refurbished as a museum in his memory.

Franklin arrived in London as agent for the State of Pennsylvania Assembly, seeking to vary the taxation arrangements in force there, but nevertheless continued to pursue his scientific researches. He had been elected a Fellow of the Royal Society in 1756 and was particularly celebrated in scientific circles for having introduced the idea of lightning conductors. In 1772 the Royal Society was asked for advice on installing them at the army's gunpowder magazines. Franklin argued, on scientific grounds, for conductors with pointed ends, but others proposed rods capped by spherical knobs. George III asked the President of the Royal Society, Sir John Pringle, that the Society's report, if in favour of lightning conductors, should opt for knobbed ones, rather than give in to the views of an American rebel. Sir John replied, 'Sire, we cannot reverse the laws and operations of nature,' for which temerity he lost his presidency within a few weeks.

Halfway down Craven Street on the right is Craven Passage and where it emerges on Northumberland Avenue is the SHERLOCK HOLMES pub [2]. The purpose of stopping here is gastronomic rather than scientific.

Sherlock Holmes was the first scientifically-minded detective of either fact or fiction so take the opportunity of seeing the reconstructed Baker Street study at the top of the stairs leading from the main bar. Note the 'chemical corner' beneath the first observation window. To find out what Holmes was doing with that Leibig condenser, distillation flask and Kipp's apparatus, you must reread *A Study in Scarlet*, *The Sign of Four* and a couple of Dr Watson's shorter reports.

Afterwards, go up Northumberland Avenue and cross the road to Trafalgar Square. Remaining on that (eastern right-hand) side, go up the steps on the north side of the Square. The terrace at the top [3] is flagged in pink and white. The white squares of Portland Stone have weathered badly, but the shells in them, significantly less eroded than the

Top: The inn sign of The Sherlock Holmes public house, in Northumberland Street.

Above: The Portland Stone paving on the north side of Trafalgar Square.

surrounding stone matrix, are the remains of Jurassic oysters which bred prolifically on what is now England's south coast 150 million years ago. Cross over the road to the east side of the National Gallery and walk round to make a brief visit to the National Portrait Gallery (NPG) [4].

Obtain a map of the Gallery at the reception desk and set out to meet some of the characters who re-appear later in the walk; this will take about 30 minutes. Specially recommended are a portrait of Newton (physicist and mathematician) in Room 4 (on the top floor); an oil portrait of Cook (cartographer and naturalist) and medallions of Benjamin Franklin (physical scientist) and William Hunter (surgeon) in Room 11; a portrait of Davy (chemist) and a medallion of Brande (chemist) in Room 14; a miniature of Davy in Room 15; portraits of Faraday (physical scientist), Darwin (biologist) and Tyndall (physicist) in Room 16; a portrait of John Franklin (navigator) in Room 17; and a drawing of William Bragg (physicist) in Room 27. Be warned that the NPG is as beguiling as the Sirens' Song; fight hard against being seduced by the display there.

Turn left behind the NPG into Orange Street and after passing Long's Court, turn right into St Martin's Street. NEWTON lived in a house in this street on a site [5] now occupied by a branch of the Westminster Public Libraries. Continuing into Leicester Square, note the busts of NEWTON by the Newton Gate [6] in the south-west corner of the square and of JOHN HUNTER, the great anatomist, in the south-east corner by the Hunter Gate [7].

In both these busts the noses have been eaten away as if by syphilis but actually by acid rain. Syphilis sufferers were for many years treated at St John's Hospital, the building [8] with the ornate Dutch gable in Lisle Street and facing you if you look up Leicester Street, but the service has recently been moved to another hospital.

Bust of John Hunter (1728-1793), anatomist and surgeon, in the south-east corner of Leicester Square.

From 1783, Hunter lived in a house on the east side of Leicester Square, on a site now occupied by the Odeon cinema. He also bought the house behind, and on the land in between he built his great museum. At his death it held 17,000 specimens of medical and biological interest. It became the foundation of the Hunterian Museum of the Royal College of Surgeons in Lincoln's Inn Fields (see p.91).

In the bar of the pub, The Moon Under Water, next to the Odeon cinema, are prints of Newton, Hunter, and various worthies associated with Leicester Square. Other prints depict some of the former popular places of entertainment in the square. One of these was the Royal Panopticon of Science and Art, 'an Institution for Scientific Exhibitions and for Promoting Discoveries in Arts and Manufactures', on the site where the Odeon cinema now stands, and another was the Panorama. Continuing in front of the cinema to the north-east corner of the square, go up Leicester Place. The church of Notre Dame de France, on the right, shows what is left of the Panorama.

The Panorama, erected in 1794, was the first purpose-built venue for one of the most popular entertainments of the nineteenth century, a picture-in-the-round. Although in some examples, but not this one, attempts were made to introduce movement, the pictures were essentially static. Audiences were surrounded by two or three scenes in succession, hauled into place by ropes and pulleys. The Panorama eventually fell out of favour and the building was consecrated as the French church in London in 1865. It was bombed in 1940, but the church was rebuilt on the Panorama's foundations, using some of the original walls. The circular structure and the dimensions have remained unchanged and give a precise idea of what the original building was like.

The former St John's Hospital, Lisle Street, in the course of its conversion into a popular Chinese restaurant.

Top: The statue of Athene above the portico of the Athenaeum, Waterloo Place.

Above: Plaque commemorating William Hunter in Great Windmill Street, above the stage door of the Lyric Theatre.

Opposite: Statue of Captain Robert Scott (1868-1912), antarctic explorer, in Waterloo Place.

Turn left at the end of Leicester Place into Lisle Street, passing the former St John's Hospital [8] (now a Chinese restaurant) and thence, turning right, to Shaftesbury Avenue. Here turn left and then take the second turn on the right into Great Windmill Street. A few yards up on the right-hand side, just past the stage door of the Lyric Theatre, a blue plaque marks the site [9] of WILLIAM HUNTER's Anatomy School and Museum.

William Hunter, John's older brother, moved his school here from Chelsea in 1770. Under William's direction and with John as assistant it was Europe's leading private academy of anatomical science until William's death in 1783. The building to the left of the site was from 1930 until 1980 the Windmill Theatre, renowned for reviews with naked girls; under the laws then in force, the girls were not allowed to move when on stage and so were displayed as immobile as the naked corpses in Hunter's dissecting rooms.

Return down Great Windmill Street, turn right into Shaftesbury Avenue and cross Piccadilly Circus to the lower end of Regent Street. This leads into Waterloo Place and, before crossing Pall Mall, note the statue [10] by A. G. Walker of FLORENCE NIGHTINGALE, the Lady with the Lamp in the hospitals serving the wounded of the Crimean

War. Later she was the reformer of nursing education and of hospital design, and
a pioneer of public health practice. (The
adjacent statue is of SIDNEY HER-
BERT, Secretary of War at the time, who
assisted Florence Nightingale with her
reforms.) Cross Pall Mall and proceed in
front of the Athenaeum, the building surmounted by the gilded statue of Athene.

This (strictly private) club for scientists,
clerics and senior civil servants, had
Faraday as a founding member and its first
secretary.

Immediately beyond the Athenaeum
stands a statue [11] of SIR JOHN FRANKLIN
(by Matthew Noble). Opposite him, on the
other side of Waterloo Place, is a statue [12] of
CAPT. ROBERT SCOTT (by his wife,
Lady Scott).

John Franklin died in the snows of the
Arctic in 1847, seeking the North-West
Passage, and Scott died in the snows of the
Antarctic in 1912, returning from the South
Pole. Although explorers are not necessarily
scientists, both of these made useful scientific observations, enlarged people's minds
and their view of the world, and opened up
territories where permanent scientific stations are now placed.

Accepting explorers along with scientists, if you have the time, go down the Duke of
York Steps at the end of Waterloo Place; across The Mall and about 100 m to the left
stands a statue [13] of CAPT. JAMES COOK (by Thomas Brock).

Cook established the geography of Australasia on his first voyage to that continent, when he was
accompanied by Joseph Banks from whom he learned sufficient botany to conduct his own plant-
collecting forays, as a result of which he was elected a Fellow of the Royal Society. But then, on his
return from his second voyage there, he was killed by natives in Hawaii, in February 1779.

If you cross The Mall to see his statue you must then recross and beware of being killed by London natives in their motorcars. At the top of the Duke of York Steps, turn westwards along Carlton House Terrace. The Royal Society at 6-9 Carlton House Terrace [14] has premises normally open only to Fellows of the Society, although members of the public are admitted to some of the lectures and meetings held there.

Turn right into Carlton Gardens, walk across Pall Mall, continue across St James's Square and up Duke of York Street, turning left into Jermyn Street. Before moving to the house in St Martin's Street, NEWTON lived in a house on the site of 87 Jermyn Street [15], marked now by a blue plaque. Along Jermyn Street, turn right and go up Duke Street to Piccadilly.

Across Piccadilly and directly opposite Duke Street is Burlington House [16]. Around the court-yard, clockwise from the entrance archway, are the Linnean Society, the Royal Astronomical Society together with the London Mathematical Society, the Society of Antiquaries, the Royal Academy of Arts, the Royal Society of Chemistry (library and some offices only) and the Geological Society. All of these, except for the Linnean Society and the Royal

Above: Plaque marking the residence of Sir Isaac Newton in Jermyn Street.

Below: Entrance to the Royal Society of Chemistry library and offices in Burlington House, Piccadilly.

Academy of Arts, are open only to members unless arrangements have been made beforehand.

If you wish to enter the premises of the Linnean Society, telephone beforehand (071-434 4479). You will then be able to visit the elegant library and also see specimens from the original collection of Linnaeus, of whom a portrait hangs in the hall. If no meeting is in progress, you may be able to obtain permission from the Secretary to look round the lecture hall. It was here that the first public account of the theory of evolution, which had been developed by DARWIN and WALLACE, was given on 1 July 1858.

Leaving Burlington House, turn right along Piccadilly and take the second turn on the right into Albemarle Street, just before the far end of which, on the right-hand side, is the Royal Institution [17]. Among the Directors of this pre-eminent scientific centre have been DAVY, FARADAY, TYNDALL, and WILLIAM BRAGG, all of whose likenesses you may have seen at the NPG, and also LAWRENCE BRAGG (William's son), DEWAR, RAYLEIGH, RIDEAL, PORTER and many others. (BRANDE, whom you may also have seen at the NPG, worked here.) If you have arrived here before 4 p.m., do not fail to visit FARADAY's Laboratory and Museum (see p.34) in the basement of the building. The remainder of the building, with its fine libraries and lecture theatres, is not normally accessible to members of the public. They are, however, welcomed at the famous Friday evening discourses.

Here the walk ENDS.

Statue in The Mall of Captain James Cook (1728-1779), explorer, navigator, cartographer and botanist.

EAST MARYLEBONE (THE PORTLAND ESTATE)

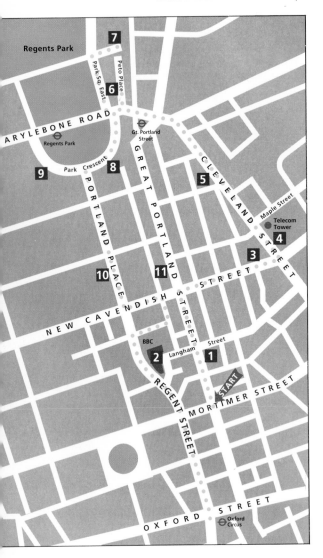

START at the corner of Mortimer Street and Great Portland Street, outside the George public house, for a walk lasting about an hour and a half. It is probably best to remain outside the George since at Broadcasting House, just round the corner in Langham Place, the BBC folk refer to the George, their local pub, as the 'Gluepot'.

> The name 'Gluepot' seems to have been given to the George by Sir Henry Wood who observed that members of his orchestra, playing in the Queen's Hall in Regent Street (bombed in 1940), found it difficult to unstick themselves from the barstools as the end of their rest periods approached.

About 100 m up Great Portland Street on the right, at No.94, on the corner of Langham Street [1], is a plaque marking the residence of DAVID EDWARD HUGHES, the inventor of the microphone. To the left, along Langham Street, you can see the side of Broadcasting House [2], which contains many hundreds of the modern versions of Hughes' invention.

Opposite above: The inn sign of The George public house, known as the 'Gluepot', in Great Portland Street.

Opposite below: The BT Tower at the corner of Cleveland Street and Maple Street.

Hughes was born in London in 1830 and emigrated with his parents to the U.S.A. He became a professor of music in Kentucky at the age of 19, but gave up music after a few years to develop his type-printing telegraph. This was patented in 1855, brought into use by the American Telegraph Company and later by most European countries, though not by the British. Hughes nevertheless settled in London in the early 1870s. Hughes improved Alexander Graham Bell's telephone system by his invention of the carbon granule microphone. He was elected a Fellow of the Royal Society in 1880 and received its gold medal five years later. Hughes probably anticipated Hertz's discovery of radio waves but failed to publish his results.

Continue up Great Portland Street and turn right into New Cavendish Street. On the left you pass the (private) Healthlinx Medical Screening Centre and then the building that houses the science and engineering departments of the University of Westminster [3].

This University was founded in 1838 as the Royal Polytechnic Institute by SIR GEORGE CAYLEY, the true inventor of the aeroplane and an important contributor to the theory of aerodynamics. The Institute was re-founded as the Polytechnic in 1881 by Quintin Hogg and acquired its present status in 1992.

Turn left into Cleveland Street, but note on the opposite corner the building marked as the Middlesex Hospital Medical School. It was formerly an independent medical school of the University of London, but is now merged with University College Medical School.

Proceeding up Cleveland Street, you hardly notice the BT Tower [4] soaring above a base just behind the corner with Maple Street, on the right. This 189 m high structure is the hub of the British Telecommunications plc radiocommunications network. Some years ago, when it was called the Post Office Tower, the public had access to a revolving restaurant 140 m above ground which can be seen as part of the thick disc near the summit of the tower — but terrorist action obliged the authorities

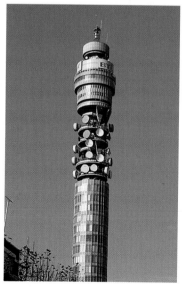

to discontinue public admission. Further up Cleveland Street, at No 141 [5] on the left, a plaque commemorates the stay there over the years 1812-1815 of SAMUEL MORSE, the inventor of the Morse Code.

Morse was born in Massachusetts in 1791, graduated from Yale in 1810 and lived in Cleveland Street as a student of painting. On his return to the U.S.A., he established the National Academy of Design and became its first president. He was professor of painting and sculpture at the City University of New York at the time of the invention of his code and of the apparatus enabling its use in telegraphy, which he demonstrated in the University in 1837. Morse lost most of his money in developing his inventions before he was able to send the first telegram — from Washington to Baltimore — in 1844. However, the commercial applications of the devices made him a rich man at the time of his death in 1872.

At the top of Cleveland Street, turn left and cross at the traffic lights to reach the northern side of Marylebone Road. Passing No.2, which houses the offices and some testing laboratories of the Consumers Association, turn right into Peto Place. This brings you to the back of a very large buttressed Georgian building [6] of 1823, which still houses the auditorium and mechanisms of the display sensation of that year, the Diorama.

Opposite: The Royal College of Physicians, from Peto Place.

Below: Park Square East, showing on the left the former entrance to the Diorama.

The audience in the Diorama viewed pictures thrown on to a screen. By the use of blinds, coloured screens and curtains, controlled by an elaborate system of pulleys and cords working to a scripted programme, dynamic effects were produced which enchanted the audiences unused to mechanized entertainments. Furthermore, the whole auditorium could be rotated between two vast viewing tunnels, allowing the display in one to be re-arranged while the audience was viewing the other.

From the end of Peto Place, you can view the handsome structure (designed by Denis Lasdun) of the Royal College of Physicians [7]. But you cannot get past the railings to look at it more closely. To do that and also, by making prior arrangements with the Librarian (071-935 1174), to see the magnificent collection of portraits there (see p. 156), you must backtrack to Marylebone Road, turn right and then right again up Park Square East. In the garden of the Royal College is a bust of THOMAS LINACRE (1460-1524), scholar, physician and first president of the Royal College. Also in the garden is a plaque noting that FRANK BUCKLAND (1826-1880), a physician and naturalist, lived in a house on that site. In St Andrew's Place, against which the Peto Place railings stopped, apart from the Royal College, there are the offices of the British Geriatric Association, the Faculty of Pharmaceutical Medicine, and the Faculty of Public Health Medicine.

Returning down Park Square East towards Marylebone Road, you pass what was once the entrance to the Diorama. And on the pavement you may like to note the elegant lampposts of the electric street lights. They are emblazoned with the cypher of William IV and were originally gas lamps — among the earliest to be installed in London in what was, in the 1830s, the most fashionable area on London's outskirts.

Crossing Marylebone Road, you walk about 40 m to reach 12 Park Crescent where JOSEPH LISTER lived [8].

Lister (1827-1912) studied medicine in London but on graduating was advised to continue his education in Edinburgh, then the world's foremost centre of surgery. There he began a series of important studies in anatomy and physiology, especially on musculature and blood flow, which won him election as a Fellow of the Royal Society and appointment as Regius Professor of Surgery at Glasgow. But he is best remembered for the introduction of asepsis into operating theatres by the profuse use of carbolic acid. By this means, mortality after surgery was vastly reduced. Lister was highly honoured, served as President of the Royal Society and President of the Royal College of Surgeons and was awarded the Order of Merit.

Plaque marking the home of Lord Lister in Park Crescent.

To continue round Park Crescent, it may be necessary, because of the traffic, to go down Portland Place as far as the traffic lights and cross there. If you then return to Park Crescent, you will find a plaque on No.19 [9], marking it as once the home of SIR CHARLES WHEATSTONE, although the house is now without an entrance door.

Wheatstone (1802-1875) was Professor of Physics at King's College London and a Fellow of the Royal Society from 1837. His name is immortalized in the instrument used in all electrical laboratories, from school level to research level, the Wheatstone Bridge, which in fact he did not devise and to which he made no claim. He was, however, a prolific inventor — especially of a telegraph which preceded Morse's, of other telegraphic apparatus, and of various musical instruments including the concertina. He is also remembered for having funked a lecture at the Royal Institution in April 1846. Waiting outside the auditorium for the clock to strike before the Friday Evening Discourse he was due to deliver, his nerve failed and he bolted down the stairs and out into Albemarle Street. Faraday was obliged to step into his place and give an extempore lecture. Since that date, lecturers at the Royal Institution Discourses are always guarded by a porter in the minutes before they are due to appear, to prevent a repetition of the embarrassment.

Adjacent to Wheatstone's house, 20-26 Park Crescent provide the offices of the Medical Research Council.

Go back to the centre of Park Crescent and turn right, down Portland Place. On the island in the centre of the road, opposite No.79, is a memorial to LISTER, his bust (by

Thomas Brock) atop the column. On the left side of Portland Place, Nos.76-78 house the offices of the City and Guilds of London Institute, one of the leading organizations for the supervision of standards and examinations in British and overseas technical colleges. On the right-hand side, at No.59, are the offices of the Biochemical Society and at No.41 the Ciba Foundation [10].

The Ciba Foundation (071-636 9456), established in 1947 through the initiative of Dr R. Käppeli, Managing Director of Ciba, the Swiss pharmaceutical company, opened its doors in 1949. At the opening ceremony, Lord Beveridge said it was not a laboratory for mixing compounds, but one for mixing scientists. The Foundation organizes inter-disciplinary symposia, mainly on health topics, maintains a library, provides accommo-dation for overseas scientists visiting London, and runs a scientific information centre. The symposia (and other meetings) are strictly limited to the invited participants. The library, with a very useful collection of books and journals dealing with medicine and basic medical sciences as well as the Oppenheimer Collection of medical biogra-phies, is open (on weekdays, 9.00-18.00) to all with a professional interest in those sub-jects. The twelve rooms that comprise the accommodation facilities are firstly for par-ticipants attending the symposia, but when not in use for that purpose they may be booked by other visiting scientists at a mod-est charge. And the Media Resource Service is a unique enterprise offering connection between enquirers, especially from the press, television, etc., to scientific specialists who can offer fact or opinion on the matter at issue.

The west side of Park Crescent, with the plaque marking the home of Sir Charles Wheatstone.

Cross Portland Place and turn right, past No.36 which houses the British Institute of Radiology, the professional association of radiologists and also of physi-cists and other scientists who work on radi-ological problems. Turn left into New Cavendish Street. From the corner of Hallam Street can be seen on the left the house with a large bowed front, No.44, in which are the offices of the General Medical Council [11].

Turn right into Hallam Street, and again turning right and then left at the bottom brings you to the front of Broadcasting House [2], the headquarters of the BBC. Turn left into Regent Street. Now continue to Oxford Circus where the walk ENDS.

Alternatively, turn first left along Mortimer Street if you wish to make the experiment of checking whether the George merits the nickname of 'Gluepot'. Then eventually make your way back to Oxford Circus.

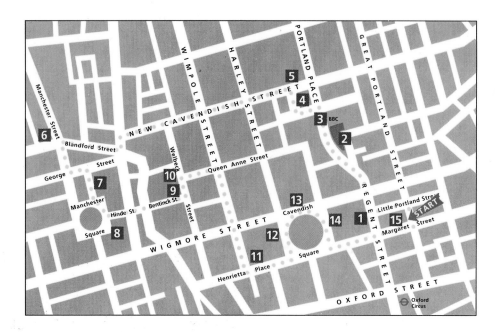

WALK NO.3
WEST MARYLEBONE (THE CAVENDISH-HARLEY ESTATE)

From Oxford Circus underground station, go east along Oxford Street, turn left into Great Portland Street to the START of the walk on the corner of Great Portland Street and Margaret Street. The walk takes about an hour and before you start it you may like to call at the Cock public house for a pint of beer. Whether you do or not, the walk proceeds up Great Portland Street and then turns left at the next corner into Little Portland Street. On the other side of Regent Street is the main building of the University of Westminster [1]. Cross Regent Street, turn right in front of the University, and facing you then is Broadcasting House [2], the headquarters of the BBC. Continue on the same side of the street, following a zigzag left and right and so up into Portland Place. In the centre of the road, opposite No.11 (offices of the section of the British Council dealing with films and television programmes), is a fine statue of QUINTIN HOGG [3].

Hogg was a philanthropist and education reformer. The Royal Polytechnic Institute, founded by Cayley in 1838, was in financial difficulties when Hogg in 1881 re-founded it as the Polytechnic in Regent Street. This was the forerunner of the University of Westminster, with its distinguished science and engineering departments. Hogg had the misfortune to die in the Polytechnic, of 'accidental asphyxiation'; he was taking a bath in an unventilated room in the building and succumbed to fumes coming from the gas-fired water heater.

Opposite above: Plaque marking the home of Charles Stanhope in Mansfield Street.

Opposite below: The entrance to Broadcasting House, headquarters of the BBC.

Continue and turn left into Duchess Street, and then turn right into Mansfield Street. At No.7 are the offices of the British Veterinary Association and at No.15 the offices of the Royal College of Midwives. A plaque on No.20 marks it as the home of CHARLES STANHOPE [4].

Stanhope (1753-1816) pursued both scientific and political careers. He wrote, aged 17, a treatise on pendulums, which won a prize from the Academy in Stockholm and election in 1772 as a Fellow of the Royal Society. He made several inventions, including methods of steam-powered navigation and a stereotype printing system which was taken up by the Clarendon Press, Oxford, and used there for a century. He also devised an improved microscope lens and a mechanical calculator and wrote several science books. In politics he was a radical Whig, chairman of the Revolution Society, an enthusiastic supporter of the aims of the French revolution and was regularly addressed as Citizen Stanhope. Supposedly in this connection, a mob set fire to his house on 10 May 1794, although Stanhope insisted they had been paid to do so by his Tory opponents. Not for reasons of political theory but quite simply because he disliked them, he disinherited all his children.

Directly across the road, at 61 New Cavendish Street [5], a plaque marks it as the home of Alfred Waterhouse, the architect of the Natural History Museum (see p. 72). It now houses the Institute of Petroleum.

The Institute, with 7,600 members, is a leading European centre for the advancement of technical knowledge relating to the international oil and gas industries. It has a library and information service accommodated in spectacularly beautiful rooms and open to members of the public (Mon-Fri 9.30-17.00).

Opposite: Statue of Quintin Hogg (1845-1903), educational reformer and founder of the Polytechnic, Regent Street, now the University of Westminster.

Left: Plaque on the house in Blandford Street where Michael Faraday lived when apprenticed as a bookbinder.

At 63 New Cavendish Street is the Institute of Psychoanalysis. Continue left from Mansfield Street down New Cavendish Street, crossing Harley Street, particularly favoured by doctors, and Wimpole Street, similarly favoured by dentists. Further down New Cavendish Street are three shops (Daniels at No.41, Seward at No.31 and Downs at No.38), which sell medical and surgical instruments — among the last shops in London to do so.

At the end of New Cavendish Street, turn left and then right into Blandford Street. At No.48, just beyond the right-hand corner with Manchester Street, is a plaque noting that MICHAEL FARADAY lived there [6] as an apprentice.

Mr George Riebau was the newsagent and bookseller who owned the house in the eight years from 1804 when Faraday (1791-1867) lived in it. Faraday was first Riebau's errand boy and then his apprentice bookbinder. By reading the books he was binding, Faraday's interest in science was awakened. The gift, by a Mr Dance, one of Riebau's customers, of tickets to Davy's lectures at the Royal Institution determined Faraday to make a life in science. He presented Davy with the notes he had made of the lectures, neatly written, beautifully illustrated, and bound by himself. This eventually persuaded Davy to offer Faraday a post at the Royal Institution, where his work established him as perhaps the greatest ever experimental scientist.

Now reverse direction and turn right, down Manchester Street, left into George Street, behind the building housing the Wallace Collection, and right into Spanish Place [7]. This small diversion is made in homage to Faraday, who recalled that in his early teens he played marbles here. Proceed into Manchester Square.

> If you have time, you may care to visit the Wallace Collection, where you can see a miniature portrait in wax of Benjamin Franklin [Room 6] and some very high-quality European and Persian armour [Rooms 8-11] (see p. 153).

In the south-east corner of Manchester Square is a plaque marking the house, No.3, where lived JOHN HUGHLINGS JACKSON [8].

> Jackson (1835-1911) was a neurologist at the London Hospital and the National Hospital for Nervous Diseases. He did important work on epilepsy and aphasia and his name is perpetuated in Jackson's Seizure (a type of epileptic attack) and Jackson's Syndrome (appearing in some forms of one-sided paralysis). He became a Fellow of the Royal Society in 1878.

Leave Manchester Square by Hinde Street, a few metres to the left of Jackson's house, and proceed across as it becomes Bentinck Street. The plaque on No.7 commemorates EDWARD GIBBON (1737-1792), the historian who, it is curious to note, attended Hunter's anatomy lectures as a way of relaxing during the writing of *Decline and Fall of the Roman Empire*. At the end of Bentinck Street, turn left into Welbeck Street. No.53 houses the offices of the Society of Chiropodists and Podiatrists. A plaque at No.50 marks it as the house of PATRICK MANSON [9].

> Manson (1844-1922) is noted in the plaque as the father of modern tropical medicine. This is perhaps hard on generations of eastern physicians, but it was Manson who clearly demonstrated that insects could be vectors of diseases. He worked in China for many years and while there showed that the organism responsible for elephantiasis was carried by a species of mosquito. He founded what is now the London School of Hygiene and Tropical Medicine and was elected a Fellow of the Royal Society in 1900.

Two houses along, at No.48 Welbeck Street, is a plaque to mark the house [10] of THOMAS YOUNG.

The house contained the surgery in which Young (1773-1829) practised as a physician for the first quarter of the nineteenth century. During the same period, this astonishing polymath also revived the wave theory of light by his famous 'double slit experiment', developed the theory of the capillarity of liquids, and introduced what is now called Young's Modulus to describe the elasticity of threads and wires. In addition, he was a renowned Egyptologist and paralleled Champollion's work on the decipherment of the Rosetta Stone. He was elected a Fellow of the Royal Society in 1794.

Above: Hertford House, Manchester Square, containing the Wallace Collection.

Opposite: The Royal College of Nursing, Cavendish Square.

Cross Welbeck Street, opposite Young's house, into Queen Anne Street and then turn right into Wimpole Street. Although Wimpole Street is the dentists' street, No.1 houses the Royal Society of Medicine [11] — location of many medical meetings and conferences and containing the best library of current medicine in London. Turn left along Henrietta Place and then left and clockwise round Cavendish Square. At No.20 are the offices of the Royal College of Nursing. A plaque at No.18 marks the house of RONALD ROSS [12].

The work begun by Manson was continued by Ross (1857-1932). While serving in India from 1881 until 1899, Ross was able to show that malaria was transmitted by the *Anopheles* mosquito. For this work he was elected a Fellow of the Royal Society in 1900 and was awarded the Nobel Prize for Medicine in 1902.

It is probably safest to stay on the inner side of the square while noting on No.15 the plaque marking the house of JONATHAN HUTCHINSON [13].

Hutchinson (1828-1913) spent most of his professional life as a surgeon at the London Hospital, with special expertise in ophthalmology, dermatology and neurology. No particular discovery attaches to his name but he was a power in the academic and surgical worlds, F.R.S. from 1882, and President of the Royal College of Surgeons in 1889. He instructed that his tombstone should describe him as 'a man of hope and forward-looking mind'.

Finally, No.5 [14] bears a plaque to QUINTIN HOGG whose statue was seen earlier, in Portland Place. Now turn left into Margaret Street. After crossing Regent Street, you pass the West End branch of the National Blood Transfusion Service [15].

If you began the walk with a pint of beer at the Cock, you may consider returning most of it in the form of a pint of blood donated here. Doing so will also gain you a cup of tea and a quiet rest on a recuperation couch.

A few more paces brings you back to the Cock on the corner of Great Portland Street, where the walk ENDS.

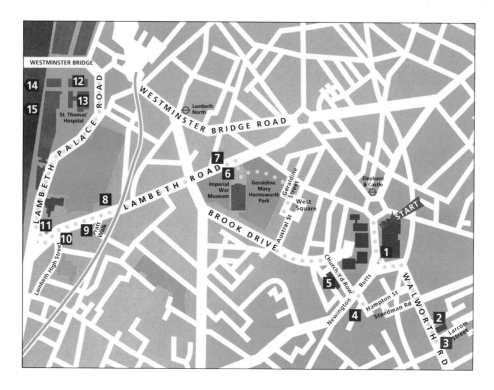

WALK NO.4
THE LAMBETH WALK AND MUSEUMS

The progressive part of this walk, actually covering the route (about 2.5 miles, 4 km), should take about an hour and a half. However, there are five museums on the way and it is a good idea to plan beforehand which, if any, of these you wish to include.

START at Elephant and Castle station, underground or rail. Emerging, turn left towards Walworth Road. Both stations are directly connected to the shopping centre complex and a plaque on an outer wall of the complex [1] as the road turns leftwards notes that MICHAEL FARADAY was born nearby. However, the walk later comes much nearer to Faraday's birthplace. In about a third of a mile (600 m), you come to the Cuming Museum [2].

The Cuming Museum is open Tuesdays-Saturdays 10.00-17.00 and we recommend that you choose a time for the walk that allows a brief visit. In this small museum, you will find the Faraday family bible with the only contemporary record of Faraday's birth. Also on display is a small hand dynamo used by Faraday in his experiments, one of his pocket watches, some photographs of him, and a few other mementoes.

The museum stands on the corner of Larcom Street and on its wall on that street is a plaque noting that CHARLES BABBAGE was born in a house that stood on the site [3].

> Babbage (see p.164), son of a banker, was born in December 1791, into a prosperous household, just three months later than Faraday and less than 350 m from the latter's birthplace in the cottage of a poor blacksmith. Babbage went to private schools and, at the age of nineteen, to the University of Cambridge. He became a leading mathematician and was appointed Lucasian Professor of Mathematics at Cambridge, the chair occupied by Newton at the end of the seventeenth century. Faraday wrote that 'my education was of the most ordinary description, consisting of little more than the rudiments of reading, writing, and arithmetic at a common day school.' At the age of thirteen he was apprenticed to a bookbinder, but he was later employed at the Royal Institution and then went on to become one of the world's most important and successful experimental scientists (see p.167).

Above: The Cuming Museum, Walworth Road, Southwark.

Left: Plaque marking the site of the birthplace of Charles Babbage, in Larcom Street.

Go back up Walworth Road, take the first street on the left, Steedman Road, follow it round to its end, turn left into Hampton Street and follow that, too, round (bending to the right) to its end in Newington Butts [4]. This road stretches about 150 m in either direction from Hampton Street and somewhere along it (the exact location is not known) lived Faraday's parents at the time of his birth. The houses standing at that time have long been demolished.

Cross Newington Butts into a narrow lane, Churchyard Row, between a piece of open ground and the side of a building that was formerly a hostel for unemployed men and has now been converted into the London Park Hotel [5]. Continue straight on to Brook Drive, turn left there and then turn into Austral Street, the third on the right. Very suddenly the architecture changes from late nineteenth-century terraces to elegant rows of late eighteenth-century houses. Austral Street leads into West Square (built in 1791); turn left before the school and leave the square through Geraldine Street. An entranceway in the wall on the left leads across the back of a hard-surfaced football pitch into the Geraldine Mary Harmsworth Park. Continuing more-or-less in the same direction brings you under the two enormous guns that stand in front of the classical façade of the Imperial War Museum [6].

> The guns were originally mounted on battleships of the Royal Navy in the years 1915 and 1916 respectively. The Imperial War Museum well deserves a visit (see p.41). If you wish to visit it at this point, allow not less than an hour — preferably two.

Leave the park by the gate to which the guns are pointed, into Lambeth Road, and turn left. About 50 m down on the right-hand side, at 100 Lambeth Road, is a plaque marking the the home [7] of WILLIAM BLIGH (1754-1817).

> Captain Bligh was given command of the *Bounty* in 1787 with orders to obtain specimens of the bread-fruit tree from Tahiti. The idea was that he would take them to the West Indies to assist the agricultural economy of that area. During the many months the vessel was docked in Tahiti, his crew formed close liaisons with Tahitian women and so resented leaving the island that they mutinied and set Bligh and several of his companions adrift in an open boat. Bligh eventually reached land, returned to England, and set out on a second expedition to gather bread-fruit, this time with success. He also collected important botanical specimens in Tasmania, Fiji and elsewhere, as well as accumulating navigational and cartographic data. He was made a Fellow of the Royal Society and raised to the rank of Vice Admiral.

The house in Lambeth Road, formerly the home of Captain William Bligh, commander of the Bounty.

Continue in the same direction along Lambeth Road. Immediately on the right, past the railway bridge, are the offices of the Nautical Institute [8], the professional body for shipmasters, nautical surveyors, harbour masters, pilots and some other specialist seafarers. Slightly further along, on the left, on the corner of Pratt Walk, is the building containing the Metropolitan Police Forensic Science Laboratory [9], one of the country's main centres for forensic investigations. After another 175 m, on the corner of Lambeth High Street, are the offices and also the museum [10] of the Royal Pharmaceutical Society.

The Nautical Institute (the tall building on the right), in Lambeth Road.

If you can demonstrate a professional interest and wish to visit the Museum (see p.94), it is necessary to make a prior appointment with the Curator.

At the end of Lambeth Road, on the right, the former St Mary's Church has been converted to the Museum of Garden History [11].

This museum (see p.60) is open only from March to mid-December, and not on Saturdays. From the museum there is access to the recreated seventeenth-century garden, formerly part of the churchyard. However, from outside, the tombs of the Tradescant father and son and of William Bligh can be seen through the gate to the garden: Bligh's tomb is surmounted by an urn; that of the Tradescants — the seventeenth-century horticulturists — has an elaborate frieze along its sides (see p.12).

Garden in the seventeenth-century style at the Museum of Garden History, Lambeth Palace Road.

The next point of note on the walk is the Florence Nightingale Museum [12]. This can be reached most directly by turning right from Lambeth Road, past Lambeth Palace, into Lambeth Palace Road and the museum is on the left just beyond the main buildings of St Thomas's Hospital [13]. A more attractive route, however, is reached by crossing Lambeth Palace Road here and turning right along the riverside path, opposite the Palace of Westminster and behind the hospital. There are splendid vistas of the Thames from here, especially of the Houses of Parliament [14], with the members' terraces in front and Westminster Abbey behind [15]. But to reach the museum by this way, it is necessary to go as far as Westminster Bridge, turn right into Westminster Bridge Road and then, following the signs to the museum, right again into Lambeth Palace Road.

> The Florence Nightingale Museum (see p.35) gives a clear perspective of the career of a remarkable woman and medical reformer, with many interesting details of the state of hospitals and public health services a century ago.

At this point the walk ENDS. If you are exhausted after the expedition and require sustenance, you can find it either in the cafeterias in St Thomas's Hospital, to which members of the public are admitted, or else in the pub, the Florence Nightingale, across Lambeth Palace Road, on the corner to the left from the museum.

Revived by food and drink, you may like to walk across Westminster Bridge to Westminster Abbey. See how many you can find of the fifty-odd memorials that have been put here to the men of science.

AN EXCURSION

GREENWICH, THAMES BARRIER AND THE ISLE OF DOGS

Institution of Electrical Engineers, behind SS Queen Mary, *with* Waterloo Bridge *on the right.*

This excursion is a trip by boat and foot with many possible variations. This means that you must plan what you are going to do, taking into account the time available, the weather conditions, your ability to manage the public transport system of London, and so on. The excursion we recommend lasts seven or eight hours. In brief, you would take a boat* down the Thames from Charing Cross Pier to Greenwich Pier, visit the Old Observatory*, and then pause for lunch*. After lunch, there is the choice of either attending the Planetarium presentation at the Observatory or spending some time at the National Maritime Museum*. Then, returning* to Greenwich Pier, you would take a boat to the Thames Barrier. When the flood defences have been examined, you return again* to Greenwich Pier, but this time by bus*, walk under the Thames to the Isle of Dogs* and take a train* back to the city. Each asterisk mark, *, is a branch point at which a choice might be made. Where possible the choices and their consequences are indicated below.

START at Charing Cross Pier on the River Thames, directly opposite the southern exit of Embankment underground station. Here take the tour boat to Greenwich (£4.40 per adult single journey), with colourful commentary by the guide, a bar and toilets on board, and a journey time of about 55 minutes, the first boat leaving at 10.30 and thereafter at 30-minute intervals (45 minutes in winter). Alternatively, you can take a train from Charing Cross Station, above you on the right, to Maze Hill, journey time 19 minutes, fare cost £3.30 if you buy a TravelCard, which will cover some of the later journeys, but the boat journey is more interesting. There is an advantage in hearing the guide's commentary on the tour boat, but if you take this option try to catch the 10.30 boat: there is a busy schedule ahead and it is best to get started early.

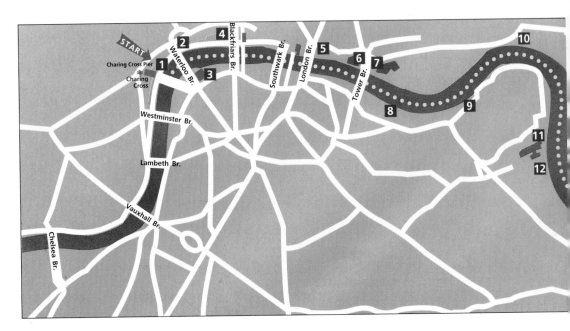

Above: The columns of the former St Paul's railway bridge.

Right: HMS Belfast, *moored in the Thames opposite the Tower of London.*

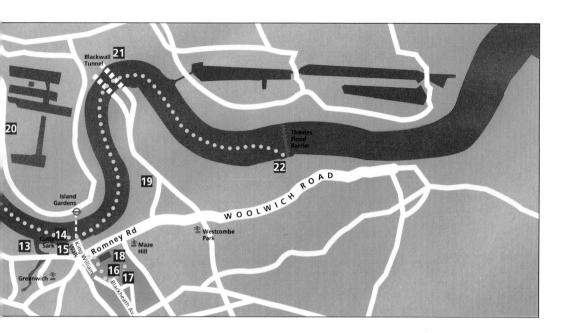

As you go down the river by boat, the following are among the sites of scientific or technological interest (L means on the left, R means on the right).

(L) The Shell Mex House, a white slightly tapered tower with a large clock, formerly the headquarters of Shell, the petroleum and chemical trading company; (L) on the river bank, Cleopatra's Needle [1], a 21 m high obelisk brought to London in 1878 from Heliopolis, the centre of sun worship in ancient Egypt; (L) behind *SS Queen Mary*, a floating pub, and immediately to the right of the Savoy Hotel, a squat and square building in red brick with white stuccoed facings, now the Institution of Electrical Engineers and on the site of the original Savoy Hill headquarters and broadcasting studios of the BBC; (L) just beyond Waterloo Bridge [first bridge of journey], the right-hand side of the building with an imposing classical façade is King's College [2], a prominent constituent of the University of London; (R) to the left of the National Theatre [3], a square tower marks the London Television Centre; (R) a thin tower down from the top of which can still be seen the logo, OXO, of the former occupants of the building, a food processing company which later merged with Brooke Bond Foods and is now part of the Unilever Group; (L) a building with a curved and pillared front, opposite the end of Blackfriars Bridge [second bridge] headquarters of Unilever [4], a major trader in foods, soaps, margarines and cosmetics and a leader in research into these; (L) and (R) columns of former St Paul's railway bridge; Alexandra railway bridge [third bridge]; Southwark Bridge [fourth bridge]; (R) Bankside power station; Cannon Street railway bridge [fifth bridge]; London Bridge [sixth bridge]; (L) Monument, a tall column surmounted by a gilded representation of flames [5], marking the place of origin of the Great Fire of London, 1666; (R) (in the river) *HMS Belfast*, a former naval cruiser, now a Museum of the Royal Navy, last saw active service in the Korean War; (L) to the left of and behind the Tower of London [6], a large but squat white tower topped by a low pyramid is the Mint, of which Newton was Master (1699-1727) although it was then housed within the Tower; Tower Bridge [seventh and last bridge] which houses a museum (see p.104); (L) immediately past Tower Bridge, St Katherine's Dock [7], opened in 1828 and designed by Telford, first President of the

Institution of Civil Engineers; (R) St Saviour's Dock [8], just to the left of Butler's Wharf; (R) about a kilometre further downriver, just beyond St Mary's Church, Rotherhithe, and the Mayflower pub, where the Mayflower docked for a week or two before sailing for the Americas in 1620, a thin 7 metre high cast-iron column which surmounts Brunel's Engine House [9] (see p.22) and provided the vent for the machines within; at this point the river crosses what was once Brunel's Tunnel, the world's first public under-water tunnel, opened in 1843 to pedestrians, but since 1869 used as a railway tunnel and now part of the London Underground Railway system; between (R) Rotherhithe Pier and (L) King Edward Memorial Park the river is passing over Rotherhithe Road Tunnel; (L), at the centre of the big bend of the river, the entrance [10] to Limehouse Basin, a dock out of which runs the Regent's Canal, called the Grand Union Canal higher up its reaches, and connecting London by water with the Midlands, the story of which can be discovered in the London Canal Museum (see p.48); (R) Greenland Dock [11], the former harbour of the Greenland whaling fleet; (R) Deadman's Dock, supposedly so-called because bubonic plague victims in the fourteenth century may have been buried nearby; (R) to the right of Convoy's Wharf, the Royal Navy rigging yards [12], behind which is an area named after Samuel Pepys, President of the Royal Society 1684-1686 and Secretary of the Admiralty for some years; (R) Deptford Creek [13]; (R) Greenwich Pier [14], the point of disembarkation, but note that just before the Pier is a small red-brick round building, joined to an identical building on the opposite bank by the Greenwich Foot Tunnel beneath the river, and that just after the Pier are the buildings of the Royal Naval College, designed by Sir Christopher Wren, President of the Royal Society 1680-1682.

In a dry dock at the Pier is the *Cutty Sark* [15], a nineteenth-century clipper, designed for the transport of tea from the Far East. This is a fine example of sailing ship technology, but we recommend you to leave visiting it until a more convenient time later in the day. Instead, carry straight on along King William's Walk, turn left into Romney Road, following the pointers to the National Maritime Museum and the Old Observatory, which after about 150 m turn you rightwards into the grounds of the museum. And here you must decide whether you wish to attend the Planetarium show, which is usually mounted at 14.00 (and also at 15.00) at the Observatory.

If yes, and if it is early enough (i.e. before about 11.15), pay a quick visit (see overleaf) to the Maritime Museum; in this case the plan is to get to the Observatory not later than noon, buy a ticket for the Planetarium show while there are still seats available, spend until about 13.00 in the Observatory, and have a light lunch in the nearby cafeteria before the Planetarium presentation.

If no, or if yes but if it's later than 11.30, it is probably best to go straight on to the Observatory, which is of particularly great scientific and historical interest. The plan for the Planetarium party is to catch up with the early birds of the previous group (see above); the plan for the others is to examine the Observatory collections and displays, but to return to the Museum for lunch soon after 13.00.

All groups should, on entering the first site, buy a 'Passport' ticket, which allows the holder into all the museums in the area. And all should plan to be back at Greenwich Pier by 15.20, in time to buy tickets for the 15.30 boat to the Thames Flood Barrier, unless travel there is to be omitted or is to be by road (bus or taxi). However, boats do not run on this part of the excursion between mid-December and mid-February. It's a good idea to telephone beforehand to check sailings (071-987 1185 and 081-305 0300).

THE OLD ROYAL OBSERVATORY (see p.79) [16]

Note: there is a stiff climb on the last 100 metres or so of the walk up to the Observatory. If this would cause you physical difficulty, it may be best to take a taxi there from the Pier.

Everyone visiting the Greenwich Old Observatory likes to stand astride the meridian, the line of zero longitude, with one foot in the eastern hemisphere and the other in the western. Do that if you will, but do not omit to visit Flamsteed House to see the beautiful octagonal observatorium, created by Christopher Wren, himself an astronomer as well as architect, for Flamsteed, the first Astronomer Royal; and also the display of timepieces including the marine chronometer by Harrison, so accurate even in stormy seas that it won its maker the Admiralty prize of £20,000 in 1773. In the neighbouring building, see Halley's mural quadrant and the Airy Transit Circle, by means of which the Greenwich Meridian is defined. And do not fail to go up into the dome of the Great Equatorial Building and see the 28 inch refractor telescope, which is the largest refractor in the U.K. and the seventh largest in the world. Wherever you are in the general area, try to be outside and within sight of the big red time ball at a few minutes to 13.00 and see it fall precisely on the hour, as it has done daily for the past 160 years.

Above: The Old Royal Observatory, Greenwich.

Opposite: The National Maritime Museum, Greenwich.

It will now be time for lunch. If you intend to see the 14.00 Planetarium presentation, which takes place in the

South Building, behind the Observatory, go for a light meal at the cafeteria on the opposite side of Blackheath Avenue to that building. Otherwise, there is a greater choice of food in the restaurant in the Maritime Museum complex.

THE PLANETARIUM [17]

The presentation here, in the dome of the South Building, is of a high standard and typically lasts for about 40 minutes. (Although the times are given here as 14.00 and 15.00, school parties can be provided with special showings in the mornings.) Beneath a glass cover in the garden adjacent to the South Building is all that remains of Sir William Herschel's 40 inch reflecting telescope, the largest in the world until 1837.

THE NATIONAL MARITIME MUSEUM [18]

If you went to the Planetarium, there would probably be no time available to visit the Maritime Museum. If not, the time you can allow depends on how long you spent over lunch. There is much to be seen here (see p.66), but if time is short, Galleries 1, 4, and 5 are specially recommended. Gallery 4 shows the work of Cook's expeditions to Australasia and the others display important collections of navigational instruments. If possible, look also at the marine archaeology display, off Gallery 10.

THE CUTTY SARK [15]

This fine old sailing ship has many items illustrating mid-nineteenth-century marine technology. You can see also that the senior officers lived in comparative luxury (during fine weather), but you don't see the crew's quarters.

Now board the boat for the Thames Barrier Cruise with more light-hearted commentary on the 25-minute journey, but see note above about winter sailings. (An option is, in Romney Road, to take a taxi or a 177 or 180 bus going eastwards to the Thames Barrier Visitors Centre, an uninteresting journey of about 4 km, taking 10-15 minutes.)

From the boat you will see (R), a little past the Royal Naval College, Trinity Hospital, a retirement home for former sailors; (R) a little further down, Greenwich Power Station [19], then a large gin distillery, behind which are large (town) gas holders; (L) the entrance to the former West India Docks and on the river front Canary Wharf and Canada Tower [20], the tallest building in Britain; (R) the low mushroom-shaped building is an air shaft for the Blackwall Road Tunnel which the river here crosses; (R) a board, close to the shore, carries a vertical line marking the crossing of the river and the Greenwich Meridian; (L) a new building surmounted by a large dish aerial (antenna) houses the offices of Reuters [21], the news and data agency.

Opposite: The Cutty Sark, *a mid-nineteenth-century tea clipper at Greenwich. On the left is the domed entrance to the Greenwich side of the foot tunnel beneath the Thames.*

Right: Canary Wharf and Canada Tower, the tallest buidling in Britain, on the Isle of Dogs.

To reach the disembarkation point at Barrier Pier [22] the tour boat passes (provided there is no imminent danger of flood) between the piers that carry the barrier gates and which tower above the boat like sightless monsters from another world. Even when seen from the bank, the immensity of the project is awesome. A visit to the Thames Barrier Visitors Centre (see p.103) provides the opportunity of finding a detailed explanation of the engineering achievement. An audio-visual demonstration provides an account of London's floods, but relatively little about defences against them.

The last boat back to Greenwich leaves at 16.00. If that hour has passed, walk up to the main road — Woolwich Road, about 400 m away — and return by taxi or by 177 or 180 bus, alighting at the stop for Greenwich Pier. Here descend, via the round, conical-roofed entrance, to the Greenwich Foot Tunnel, an engineering success of the turn of the century. There is a lift both down and up, although it is worth catching the thrill of the earlier days of the tunnel by walking down, but perhaps riding up at the other end. (Alternatively, alight from the bus near to Maze Hill station, and return to Charing Cross from there by train.)

The exit on the north side of the river brings you into the area called the Isle of Dogs and is situated directly by the Island Gardens station of the Docklands Light Railway. (A London Transport TravelCard, if you have one, is valid on this line.) Here you can catch a train to Bank, in the centre of the City and connecting with the London Underground system, for a journey of about 15 minutes. The train, which is automatic and driverless, travels on an elevated track and provides excellent views of the intensive building developments which, in a decade, have reclaimed for commercial and domestic use a vast area of abandoned dockyards, retaining the waterways themselves as historic and decorative features.

From Bank you may catch an underground train back to Embankment, or to whichever other station suits you, to bring the day's excursion to an END.

ADDRESSES

ACADEMIC INSTITUTIONS

SCHOOLS

City of London School
Queen Victoria Street, EC4V 3AL
Tel: 071-489 0291

Elizabeth Garrett Anderson School
Rising Hill Street, N1 9OG
Tel: 071-837 4389

Harrow School
5 High Street, Harrow, HA1 3HP
Tel: 081-422 2196

Michael Faraday Junior School
Portland Street, SE17 2HR
Tel: 071-277 1498

Newton Preparatory School
149 Battersea Park Road, SW8 4BX
Tel: 071-720 4091

St Paul's School
Lonsdale Road, SW13 9JT
Tel: 081-748 9162

University College School
Frognal, NW3 6XH
Tel: 071-435 2215

Westminster School
Little Dean's Yard, SW1P 3PF   Tel:
071-222 5516

UNIVERSITIES

Brunel University
Uxbridge, Middlesex, UB8 3PH
Tel: 0895 274000

City University
Northampton Square, EC1V 0HB
Tel: 071-477 8000

East London University
Longbridge Road, Dagenham, Essex,
RM8 2AS
Tel: 081-590 7722

Greenwich University
Wellington Street, Woolwich,
SE18 6PF
Tel: 081-316 8590

Guildhall University
139 Minories, EC3N 1NL
Tel: 071-320 1000

Kingston University
Penrhyn Road, Kingston-upon-
Thames, KT1 2EE
Tel: 081-547 2000

Middlesex University
All Saints, White Hart Lane,
N17 8HR
Tel: 081-362 5000

North London University
166-220 Holloway Road, N7 8DB
Tel: 071-607 2789

South Bank University
Borough Road, SE1 0AA
Tel: 071-928 8989

Thames Valley University
St Mary's Road, Ealing, W5 5RF
Tel: 081-579 5000

University of London
  Birkbeck College
  Malet Street, WC1E 7HX
  Tel: 071-580 6622
  Imperial College
  South Kensington, SW7 2AZ
  Tel: 071-589 5111
  Institute of Archaeology
  University College, Gower Street,
  WC1E 6BT
  Tel: 071-387 7050
  Institute of Cancer Research
  17a Onslow Gardens, SW7 3AL
  Tel: 071-352 8133
  Institute of Dental Surgery
  Eastman Dental Hospital,
  Gray's Inn Road, WC1X 8LD
  Tel: 071-915 1000
  Institute of Ophthalmology
  Bath Street, EC1V 9EL
  Tel: 071-608 6800
  King's College
  Strand, WC2R 2LS
  Tel: 071-836 5454
  London Hospital Medical College
  Turner Street, E1 2AD
  Tel: 071-377 7000
  London School of Economics
  Houghton Street, WC2A 2AE
  Tel: 071-405 7686
  Queen Mary College
  Mile End Road, E1 4NS
  Tel: 071-975 5555
  **Royal Free Hospital School of
  Medicine**
  Rowland Hill Street, NW3 2PF
  Tel: 071-794 0500
  Royal Holloway College
  Egham Hill, Egham, Surrey,
  TW20 0EX
  Tel: 0784 434455
  Royal Veterinary College
  Royal College Street, NW1 0TU
  Tel: 071-387 2898

  **St Bartholomew's Hospital
  Medical College**
  West Smithfield, EC1A 7BE
  Tel: 071-982 6000
  **St George's Hospital Medical
  School**
  Cranmer Terrace, SW17 0RE
  Tel: 081-672 9944
  **United Medical and Dental
  Schools of Guy's and St
  Thomas's Hospitals**
  Lambeth Palace Road, SE1 7EH
  Tel: 071-928 9292
  University College
  Gower Street, WC1E 6BT
  Tel: 071-387 7050

Westminster University
309 Regent Street, W1R 8AL
Tel: 071-911 5000

ART GALLERIES

Courtauld Institute of Art
Somerset House, Strand,
WC2R 0RN
Tel: 071-873 2526

Iveagh Bequest, Kenwood
Hampstead Lane, NW3 7JR
Tel: 081-348 1286

National Gallery
Trafalgar Square, WC2N 5DN
Tel: 071-839 3321

National Museum of Cartoon Art
185 Eversholt Street, NW1 1DD
Tel: 071-388 4326

National Portrait Gallery
St Martin's Place, WC2H 0HE
Tel: 071-306 0055

Tate Gallery
Millbank, SW1P 4RG
Tel: 071-821 1313

Victoria and Albert Museum
Cromwell Road, SW7 2RL
Tel: 071-938 8500

Wallace Collection
Hertford House,
Manchester Square, W1M 6BN
Tel: 071-935 0687

CEMETERIES

Hampstead Cemetery
Fortune Green Road, NW6 1DR
Tel: 071-435 6142

Highgate Cemetery
Swains Lane, N6 6PJ
Tel: 081-340 1834
Kensal Green Cemetery
Harrow Road, W10 4RA
Tel: 081-969 0152

CHURCHES, ETC.
Chelsea Old Church
Cheyne Walk, SW3 5DQ
Tel: 071-352 5627
St Paul's Cathedral
St Paul's Churchyard,
EC4M 8AE
Tel: 071-248 2705
Westminster Abbey
20 Dean's Yard, SW1P 3PA
Tel: 071-222 5152

HOSPITALS, ETC.
Charter Nightingale Hospital
11-19 Lisson Grove, NW1 6SH
Tel: 071-258 3828
Elizabeth Garrett Anderson
Hospital
144 Euston Road, NW1 2AP
Tel: 071-387 2501
Hammersmith Hospital
150 Du Cane Road, W12 0HS
Tel: 081-743 2030
Harefield Hospital
Hill End Road,
Harefield, UB9 6JH
Tel: 0895 823737
Northwick Park Hospital
Watford Road, Harrow, HA1 3UJ
Tel: 081-864 3232
St Thomas's Hospital
Lambeth Palace Road, SE1 7EH
Tel: 071-928 9292
St Bartholomew's Hospital
West Smithfield, EC1A 7BE
Tel: 071-601 8888
Thomas Coram Foundation
40 Brunswick Square, WC1N 1AU
Tel: 071-278 2424

LABORATORIES
PUBLICLY-FUNDED
Central Public Health Laboratory
61 Colindale Avenue, NW9 5HT
Tel: 081-200 4400
Fire Research Station
Borehamwood, Herts WD6 2BL
Tel: 081-953 6177

Jodrell Laboratory
Royal Botanic Gardens, Kew
TW9 3AB
Tel: 081-940 1171
Laboratory of the Government
Chemist
Queens Road, Teddington TW11 0LY
Tel: 081-943 7000
London Underground Scientific
Services Laboratory
Frank Pick House,
Bollo Lane, W3 8RP
Tel: 081-724 5600
Metropolitan Police Forensic
Science Laboratory
109 Lambeth Road, SE1 7LP
Tel: 071-230 6400
National Institute for Medical
Research
The Ridgeway, NW7 1AA
Tel: 081-959 3666
National Physical Laboratory
Teddington, Middlesex, TW11 0LW
Tel: 081-977 3222
National Weights and Measures
Office
Stanton Avenue, Teddington,
TW11 0JZ
Tel: 081-943 7272

PRIVATELY-FUNDED
Imperial Cancer Research Fund
44 Lincoln's Inn Fields,
WC2A 3PX
Tel: 071-242 0200
Royal National Institute for the
Blind
224 Great Portland Street,
W1N 5TB
Tel: 071-388 1266
Royal National Institute for the
Deaf
105 Gower Street, WC1E 6AH
Tel: 071-387 8033

INDUSTRIAL & COMMERCIAL
British Maritime Technology
1 Waldegrave Road, Teddington,
TW11 8LZ
Tel: 081-943 5544
Central Research Laboratory
(Thorn-E.M.I.)
Dawley Road, Hayes, UB3 1HH
Tel: 081-848 9779

Glaxo Group Research
Greenford Road, Greenford,
UB6 0HE
Tel: 081-422 3434
Hirst Research Centre (G.E.C.)
East Lane, Wembley, HA9 7PP
Tel: 081-908 9000
Elstree Way, Borehamwood,
WD6 1RX
Tel: 081-953 2030
Rhône-Poulenc (May & Baker)
Rainham Rd South, Dagenham,
RM10 7XS
Tel: 081-592 3060
Sira Group
South Hill, Chislehurst BR7 5EH
Tel: 081-467 2636
Wellcome Foundation
Langley Court, Beckenham, BR3 3BS
Tel: 081-658 2211

LEARNED SOCIETIES ,
PROFESSIONAL BODIES, ETC
British Medical Association
BMA House, Tavistock Square,
WC1H 9JP
Tel: 071-387 4499
Ciba Foundation
41 Portland Place, W1N 4BN
Tel: 071-636 9456
Gresham College
Barnard's Inn Hall, Holborn, EC1N
2HH
Tel: 071-831 0575
General Medical Council
44 Hallam Street, W1N 6AE
Tel: 071-580 7642
Geological Society
Burlington House, Piccadilly,
W1V 0JU
Tel: 071-434 9944
Institution of Civil Engineers
Great George Street, SW1P 3AA
Tel: 071-222 7722
Institution of Electrical Engineers
Savoy Place, WC2R 0BL
Tel: 071-240 1871
Institution of Marine Engineers
76 Mark Lane, EC3R 7IN
Tel: 071-481 8493
Institution of Mechanical Engineers
1 Birdcage Walk, SW1H 9JJ
Tel: 071-222 7899

Linnean Society
Burlington House, Piccadilly,
W1V 0LQ
Tel: 071-434 4479

Royal Astronomical Society
Burlington House, Piccadilly,
W1V 0NL
Tel: 071-734 4582

Royal College of Anaesthetists
48 Russell Square, WC1B 4JY
Tel: 071-813 1900

**Royal College of General
Practitioners**
14 Princes Gate, SW7 1PU
Tel: 071-581 3232

Royal College of Nursing
20 Cavendish Square, W1M 9AE
Tel: 071-409 3333

**Royal College of Obstetricians and
Gynaecologists**
27 Sussex Place, NW1 4RG
Tel: 071-262 5425

Royal College of Pathologists
2 Carlton House Terrace,
SW1Y 5AF
Tel: 071-930 5861

Royal College of Physicians
11 St Andrew's Place,
NW1 4LE
Tel: 071-935 1174

Royal College of Psychiatrists
17 Belgrave Square, SW1X 8PG
Tel: 071-235 2351

Royal College of Radiologists
38 Portland Place, W1N 3DG
Tel: 071-636 4432

Royal College of Surgeons
35 Lincoln's Inn Fields,
WC2A 3PF
Tel: 071-405 3474

Royal College of Veterinary Surgeons
32 Belgrave Square, SW1X 8QP
Tel: 071-235 4971

Royal Entomological Society
41 Queen's Gate, SW7 5HR
Tel: 071-584 8361

Royal Institution
21 Albemarle Street, W1X 4BS
Tel: 071-409 2992

Royal Pharmaceutical Society
1 Lambeth High Street, SE1 7JN
Tel: 071-735 9141

Royal Society
6 Carlton House Terrace,
SW1Y 5AG
Tel: 071-839 5561

Royal Society of Arts (RSA)
8 John Adam Street, WC2N 6EY
Tel: 071-930 5115

Royal Society of Chemistry
Burlington House, Piccadilly,
W1V 0BN
Tel: 071-437 8656

Royal Society of Medicine
1 Wimpole Street, W1M 7AA
Tel: 071-408 2119

Royal Statistical Society
25 Enford Street, W1H 1DG
Tel: 071-723 5882

Society of Apothecaries
Apothecaries Hall, Black Friars Lane,
EC4V 6EJ
Tel: 071-236 1189

LIBRARIES

British Library (see also British
Museum Library and SRIS)
96 Euston Road, NW1 2DB
Tel: 071-323 7262

British Museum Library
Great Russell Street, WC1 3DG
Tel: 071-323 557

Croydon Central Library
Katherine Street, Croydon, CR9 1ET
Tel: 081-760 5400

Ealing Public Library
103 Ealing Broadway Centre, W5 5JY
Tel: 081-840 0010

Harrow Public Library
P.O.Box 4, Civic Centre, Harrow,
HA1 2UU
Tel: 081-424 1055

Patent Office Library (see SRIS)

Science Museum Library
Exhibition Road, SW7 2DD
Tel: 071-938 8234

SRIS (Science Reference and
Information Service)
  Holborn branch
  25 Southampton Buildings,
  WC2A 1AW
  Tel: 071-323 7494
  Aldwych branch
  9 Kean Street, WC2B 4AT
  Tel: 071-323 7288

Westminster Public Library
  Leicester Square branch
  St Martin's Street, SW1E 6QP
  Tel: 071-798 2034
  Marylebone branch (medical
  Library)
  Marylebone Road, NW1 5PS
  Tel: 071-798 1039

Witt Library
Somerset House North Block, Strand,
WC2R 0RN
Tel: 071-872 0220
see also
list of learned societies and professional bodies
list of universities and colleges
museums in Chapter 1

LOCAL SCIENTIFIC SOCIETIES

Bourne Society
Hon. Sec: Roger Packham, 40 Raglan
Precinct, Town End, Caterham, Surrey
CR3 5UG Tel: 0883 349198

**Croydon Natural History and
Scientific Society**
Museum Curator: Mrs M Shaw
96A Brighton Road, South Croydon
CR2 6AD
Tel: 081-688 2720

Hampstead Scientific Society
Hon. Sec: Jim Brightwell
Tel: 081-906 2266

**Highgate Literary and Scientific
Institution**
11 South Grove, N6 6BB
Tel: 081 340 3343

Merton Scientific Society
Hon. Sec: Geoffrey Lewis :
Tel: 081-874 7019

Richmond Scientific Society
Hon. Sec: Mrs Valerie Markham
Tel: 0784 259198

MISCELLANEOUS ESTABLISHMENTS

Cock Tavern
27 Great Portland Street, W1N 5DD
Tel: 071-631 5002

Daniel Gooch
40 Porchester Road, W2 6ES
Tel: 071-221 6447

Euston Station
Euston Road, NW1 1DZ
Tel: 071-387 7070

Florence Nightingale
199 Westminster Bridge Road, SE1
7UT
Tel: 071-928 3027

The George (Gluepot)
55 Great Portland Street,
W1N 5DH
Tel: 071-636 0863

The John Baird
Fortis Green Road, N10 3HN
Tel: 081-444 8830

The John Snow
39 Broadwick Street, W1V 1FT
Tel: 071-437 1344

Paddington Station
Praed Street, W2 1ET
Tel: 071-262 6767

Royal Arsenal (inc. Royal Laboratory)
Woolwich, SE18 6ST
Tel: 081-854 2044

Royal School of Chemistry (see Imperial College)

Royal (formerly Government) School of Mines (see Imperial College)

Sherlock Holmes
10 Northumberland Street,
WC2N 5DA
Tel: 071-930 2644

Sir Alexander Fleming
16 Bouverie Place, W2 1RB
Tel: 071-723 6061

The Museum Tavern
49 Great Russell Street, WC1B 3BA
Tel: 071-242 8987

SHOPS, ETC.

Bernard Muller
344 Fulham Road, SW10 9UH
Tel: 071-352 1756

BMJ Bookshop
Burton Street, WC1H 9JR
Tel: 071-383 6244

Bonham's Auction Rooms
Montpellier Street, SW7 1HH
Tel: 071-584 9161

Broadhurst, Clarkson & Fuller
63 Farringdon Road, EC1M 3JB
Tel: 071-405 2156

Christie's Auction Rooms
8-10 King Street, SW1Y 6QT
Tel: 071-839 9060

Connelly (Vade Mecum Press)
31-35 Great Ormond Street,
WC1N 3HZ
Tel: 071-430 1394

Daniels
41 New Cavendish Street,
W1M 8EB
Tel: 071-935 4175

P. Delehar
146 Portobello Road, W11 2DZ
Tel: 071-727 9860

Dillon's
82 Gower Street, WC1E 6EQ
Tel: 071-636 1577

Science Museum
Exhibition Road, SW7 2DD
Tel: 071-938 8254

Grand Buildings,
Trafalgar Square, WC2N 5EJ
Tel: 071-839 4411

Downs
32 New Cavendish Street, W1M 8BU
Tel: 071-486 3611

Foyle's
119 Charing Cross Road, WC2H 0EB
Tel: 071-437 5660

Hamley's
188 Regent Street, W1R 6BT
Tel: 071-734 3161

Harrod's
Knightsbridge, SW1X 7XL
Tel: 071-730 1234

D. Howard
Chelsea Antiques Market,
245-253 King's Road,
SW3 5EL
Tel: 071-352 4113

Jessop
67-69 New Oxford Street,
WC1A 1DG
Tel: 071-240 6077

John Bell & Croyden
50-54 Wigmore Street, W1H 0AU
Tel: 071-935 5555

A. Middleton
12 New Row, WC2N 4LF
Tel: 071-836 7042

Modern Book Co.
19-21 Praed Street, W2 1NP
Tel: 071-402 9176

Phillip's Auction Rooms
101 New Bond Street, W1Y 0AS
Tel: 071-629 6602

Porter Nash
116 Wigmore Street, W1H 9FD
Tel: 071-486 1434

Rogers Turner Books
22 Nelson Road, SE10 9JB
Tel: 081-853 5271

Selfridges
400 Oxford Street, W1A 1AB
Tel: 071-629 1234

Seward
31 New Cavendish Street,
W1M 7RL
Tel: 071-486 7585
131 Great Suffolk Street, SE1 1PP
Tel: 071-357 6527

Sotheby's Auction Rooms
34-35 New Bond Street,
W1A 2AA
Tel: 071-493 8080

D. & E. Squire
Unit V13a,
131 King's Road, SW3 4PW
Tel: 081-946 1470

S. Talbot
65 Portobello Road, W11 2QB
Tel: 081-969 7011

Trevor Philip & Son
75a Jermyn Street, SW1Y 6NP
Tel: 071-930 2954

Wallace Heaton
127 New Bond Street, W1Y 0AB
Tel: 071-629 7511

Waterstone's
193 Kensington High Street,
W8 6SH
Tel: 071-937 8432
99-101 Old Brompton Road,
SW7 3LE
Tel: 071-581 8522

INDEX

Picture Credits